EMOTIONAL PROBLEMS
AND WHAT YOU CAN DO ABOUT THEM

First Aid to Wiser Living

EMOTIONAL PROBLEMS

AND WHAT YOU CAN DO ABOUT THEM

•

First Aid to Wiser Living

By WILLIAM B. TERHUNE, M.D.

Medical Director, Silver Hill Foundation
New Canaan, Connecticut
Associate Clinical Professor of Psychiatry,
Yale School of Medicine

WILLIAM MORROW & COMPANY, INC.
New York · 1955

Third Printing, March 1955

Copyright 1955 by William B. Terhune
Published simultaneously in the Dominion of
Canada by George J. McLeod Limited, Toronto
Printed in the United States of America
Library of Congress Catalog Card Number: 55-5311

CONTENTS

Introduction

This book is based largely on many years of experience in practicing psychiatry. Needless to say, it does not presume to cover the whole of psychiatry—a highly specialized branch of scientific medicine. It does, however, embody certain principles of personal mental hygiene and thus its suggestions are allied to psychiatry, particularly on the preventive side.

During World War II, I wrote an address entitled "Psychological First Aid." It brought such wide response that I decided to enlarge upon the theme, and to make it the basis of a book for all men and women today who need help with emotional problems.

Nervousness, emotional illness and much true mental disease are the result of ignorance as to their nature and carelessness in the practice of the principles underlying emotional health. We have long been taught simple, logical methods of preserving physical health, failure to follow which, it is generally agreed, may bring dire results. Now, with our greater knowledge of mental health, we must equally recognize the fact that many nervous illnesses can be prevented by the daily practice of mental hygiene.

Personal mental hygiene is the art and science of so directing one's actions, thoughts and feelings that they will lead to mental stability, health, happiness and efficiency.

The suggestions and techniques I offer here may seem to you so obvious, simple and necessarily true that you may say "I know all these things." But *do* you? You may have heard them, thought them, or read them, but really to know them you must apply them yourself. If the road to Hell is paved with good intentions, the signposts pointing the way are the good ideas one has never used. So this is an invitation to share experience in the science and art of living. These are the key facts gathered from many hours spent with thousands of people discussing with the psychiatrist the good and bad techniques of personal mental hygiene.

I gratefully acknowledge the valuable assistance of Miss Lillian Lathrop, psychiatric social worker, in the preparation of this manuscript.

WILLIAM B. TERHUNE, M.D.

New Canaan, Connecticut
October, 1954

"Act with honesty and sincerity under all circumstances, meet everybody with an understanding mind as well as with trust and confidence, reveal a spirit of spontaneous and unfeigned love, and there will prove to be nearly nothing in the world that will successfully resist that impact." *

—Rufus M. Jones

* Reprinted by permission of the author, Rufus M. Jones.

. *Part One* .

THE FUNDAMENTALS OF
PERSONAL MENTAL HYGIENE

I

Psychological Preparedness

It is wise to be ready for emergencies, for as we all know, it is the unexpected that is to be expected. Meeting emergencies efficiently is the result of preparedness, and knowing that one is equipped to deal with eventualities gives confidence and reduces dread of the future. Thus when something goes wrong, there is less shock and more interest in meeting a situation not totally unforeseen. Life is not so much a matter of accident and luck as it may seem, since in the course of a lifetime most people have experiences that show a repetitive quality. The way these unexpected situations are handled determines one's happiness, usefulness and place in society. Most people are well-intentioned, but in the last analysis the use of knowledge makes the difference between efficiency and inefficiency in meeting life's problems. It is axiomatic that if you do not know what to do you will probably do wrong.

The most frequent emergencies of life are psychological, not physical. Few people ever have to compress an artery, apply a tourniquet or give artificial respiration, yet everyone must meet psychological emergencies of the utmost importance to his associates and himself, emergencies upon which material and spiritual survival may depend. The suddenness and unexpectedness with which these situations arise may temporarily paralyze the thought processes. One must therefore be prepared in advance with knowledge to be able to meet such crises calmly and efficiently.

Military tacticians, realizing that history repeats itself, study the strategies of distinguished generals. But the majority of battles are fought in an individual's heart and mind, and may leave crippling wounds, many of which could have been lessened or even prevented had the individual used the techniques of personal mental hygiene. Psychiatry stands ready to teach these principles and to demonstrate appropriate techniques of daily adjustment.

Crippling psychological traumas—injuries or shocks—give rise to that form of emotional illness known as "nervousness" or a psychoneurosis. Such neurosis may be the result of faulty childhood training, inadequate preparation for life, together with undue emotional strains and mishandled mental conflicts. When untreated, this condition continues for years. Psychological traumas of long standing frequently are beyond the skill of an amateur and, like other serious injuries, should be referred to a competent physician. If the situation is beyond you, take no chances; get help! Your own life and happiness—and that of others —may be at stake.

Everyone has general ideas on the subject of how to help himself, and perhaps others, with emotional problems. Many of these are correct, but some are as mistaken as the antiquated notion that cobwebs applied to a wound will stop hemorrhage. Nearly everyone believes that he knows many psychological facts, "learned in the hard school of experience." But psychology is a science; guesses are usually wrong; experience is at best individual and limited, and if you do not know the right way you are probably badly mistaken, since the law of averages is against happenstance. Reliable conclusions can seldom be drawn from an isolated occurrence interpreted by an untrained person, and irreparable damage may result from ignorance and inexperience, however well-meaning the intention. Medically trained people have been meeting psychological emergencies for generations. Their findings have now been systematized and codified, and it is my purpose here to describe methods that have proved their effectiveness in the more usual life situations. We will discuss the emotional crises that may occur within yourself, as well as those with which you may need to cope in helping friends or members of your family.

The more frequent psychological emergencies which arise in the course of everyday living will be discussed under the following headings:

Psychological equipment
The education of self
First aid for the adult
First aid for older people
First aid for children
First aid for the adolescent

A review of principles

Techniques for meeting specific psychological emergencies

These are followed by The Mental Hygiene Creed, which summarizes the principles.

It may be accepted as truth that most people are fundamentally good. Many wish to make their own lives significant and would like to help others, but do not know how to accomplish these desires. You are well-intentioned, so are others; your associates and even your opponents believe they are in the right. In dealing with these intracacies, a knowledge of the fundamental psychological principles will help you to think objectively and to help others.

II

Psychological Equipment

You, like everyone else, will at some time in your life come up against emotional problems with which you need help. And you are very likely to be called upon to help friends or relatives in similar need. Now is the time to provide yourself with the correct mental equipment. You must develop characteristics which you possess but may have neglected. Every normal person has a certain amount of physical coordination, but it becomes a real asset only when it is trained. This is true also of mental coordination. We all have potential psychological equipment, but we must develop it and learn to use it automatically, just as we must develop technique on the piano before we can play Bach with skill. So you must develop skills in personality and acquire techniques before you can help yourself or others. Your first-aid kit must have these essentials:

Absolute integrity is a *sine qua non*. To attain this integrity you may cut no corners, steal no bases, no matter how great the temptation. Your first step is to seek the truth about yourself, or about those you want to help, realizing that truth is elusive and must be sought out. Once you have found it, adhere to it firmly.

You must have a *desire for knowledge,* an intellectual, objective curiosity, a wish constantly to find better methods of making personal adjustment. Watch the good adjusters, discover how they do it, and imitate them. Three-fourths of learning consists of imitating that which other successful and intelligent people have discovered. So try really to *understand* yourself and others, why people act as they do, what makes them tick. In general, the truth about people is simple, uncomplicated and easily understood—therefore often overlooked.

Loyalty is one of the most valuable of all sentiments— valuable to yourself and to others. Everyone has a degree of loyalty, but perhaps you have not yet developed it or learned to use it wisely. The acme of this virtue is to support all things that merit loyalty, so try to think and speak no evil of anyone. If you are helping others, build them up by mentioning their good points, no matter how great their faults. Destructive criticism indicates your awareness of your own shortcomings, which you simply evade by criticizing others. The loyal person can be trusted at all times, and—what is more important—he trusts himself. Cultivate loyalty, but be careful upon whom you bestow it, for once given, it cannot be withdrawn.

Whether a man is loyal to a good cause or to a bad cause, his own personal life has a certain general quality. Whoever is loyal, whatever be his cause, is devoted, is active; he surrenders his own self-will, controls himself, is in love with his cause and believes in it. His frame of mind has its own value for him as well as others. To live a life of loyalty, whatever one's cause, is to live in a way which is free from many well-known sources of inner dissatisfaction. Thus, inability to make decisions is often corrected by loyalty; for the cause plainly tells the loyal man what to do. Loyalty tends to unify life, to give it contour, purpose, stability.

Be always loyal, support all constructive forces. Speak for those things in which you believe, else you may lose your chance to speak freely again. In general, one need not speak against the things one does not like, since fighting evil often strengthens it by fixing attention on evil, which may then become compulsive. Conversely, fighting for good is constructive and has a tendency to smother evil. Be *for* things and not against them.

If you have a friend or relative with an emotional difficulty, *skill in listening* is an indispensable asset. It is characterized by showing more interest in others than in yourself. The good listener will ask but few questions; he speaks only to maintain the friendly atmosphere which acts as a warm poultice for drawing the other person out. A skillful listener seldom makes comments, gives little advice, and above all does not talk about his own experiences and beliefs. This requires patience, an open mind and mental flexibility. Important matters cannot be hurried; it takes time to establish a helpful relationship between a sympathetic listener and a person who needs to talk. Just as the miner in search of gold works many a panful of sand before he finds a nugget, so it is the persistently patient listener who is rewarded. An open mind is useful because —among other benefits—it attracts other people's ideas, but the mind can be kept open only if none of the corridors are blocked by fixed ideas. To help others, you must learn to give unprejudiced consideration to things you do not like; look for the truth or beauty that others believe they find. The third requirement for skilled listening, mental flexibility, indicates a willingness to exert yourself sufficiently to look at all the angles of a situation. This calls for a great deal of mental "running around," and inflexible people are too lazy to try to cover so much ground. If the world appears flat to them, it is flat—because they are not willing to travel a bit and investigate someone else's opinion that it is round. As a corollary, with mental flexibility goes a willingness to admit error ungrudgingly and, if necessary, frequently.

Listen, and the truth will reveal itself in small pieces, not only to yourself but to the person who is talking. Help him to learn to recognize and discard the debris, and fit together the factual details until the design begins to become apparent, though parts are obviously missing. As a matter of fact, it is the missing parts, the things a person does not say, but comes gradually to realize are true, that are usually most important.

"I will sing with the spirit, and I will sing with the understanding also," said St. Paul. *An understanding spirit,* desirable though it would be in everyone, is absolutely necessary for anyone who wants to help himself and others psychologically. People seek money, fame and position, hoping thus to outfit themselves attractively in the sight of others. An understanding spirit would be a better goal, but in the quest for transient material success this enduring quality of personality is too often forgotten. Understanding yourself is largely the result of *wanting* to enough. To understand another, it is necessary to put yourself in his place, to try to feel as he does, to see things as he sees them. Understanding does not depend upon sympathy, which is a poor substitute for putting yourself in another's place—since sympathy may encourage self-pity, the most malignant of all sentiments. All people have a deep need to be understood. To understand, it is necessary to live mentally on the level of others, and to feel with them. Thus only can one assuage another person's aloneness— the most painful void in man's life.

What a comfort it is to feel that someone understands you—not only your weaknesses but your strengths—best of all, your potential strength.

Tolerance is not only a tool but the hallmark identifying a sterling character, an individual free of the dross of prejudice, one who gives to others the same complete freedom to believe and to live as he truly thinks right for himself. In dealing with yourself, as with others, tolerance is a necessity for it clears the atmosphere so that one may see far into the distance. First recognize the advantages of being tolerant, then wish to be tolerant and try to become so. Seek and obliterate ruthlessly all intolerance that you can find within yourself. Realize that every intolerance is wrong and that, as long as even one remains, it will obscure your vision in some direction.

The intolerant, prejudiced, opinionated or dominating person makes others miserable and is, at the same time, not functioning at his best for himself. His fault exists only as a pathological attempt to protect a weak ego in a small spirit. Once again, be *for* things and not against them.

Efficiency in one's own life is important since much suffering and misunderstanding is due to careless inefficiency. As a nurse must be able to put a bandage on securely and quickly, so you, who are trying to help yourself or your friends, must use the appropriate emotional adhesive, must be able to apply an idea deftly so it will stick. Learn to be efficient; do things the easiest and simplest way; minimize the effort involved; enjoy doing each job better. Much of the satisfaction in life lies in accomplishing a purpose simply and efficiently. Once you know *how* to do it, "easy does it," and life becomes increasingly satisfying. The height of efficiency is casual efficiency. Try to accomplish your purpose with the least and best effort— and help others to do likewise.

Humility is the mark of a truly great personality; no small person was ever humble in spirit. The humble person acknowledges failure and success without being unduly cast down by the one or set up by the other. He treats criticism and flattery in a similar manner. He knows that human action is imperfect more often than not, and that he is responsible for his purpose but not altogether for the results—provided the purpose has been diligently and efficiently sought. People with true humility are usually kind, and everyone feels a binding affection for them. Humility is a conspicuous trait in the character of a mature person.

Good judgment is an invaluable asset and to possess it should be everyone's goal. Fortunately, good judgment can be acquired through training and practice. Thus, take time to think through even an emergency, then check and recheck facts and decisions. When called upon to handle an emotional emergency of your own, ask yourself: "Does what I am about to do show good judgment? Would a jury of good, wise, and experienced men and women agree that this is the wise thing to do, for everyone concerned?" Start each day with this prayer: "May I use good judgment in both my small and my large acts."

Try to supply others with the judgment that they need in an emergency, then help them gradually to use good judgment for themselves. Try to make them independent but give assistance until they are strong enough to stand alone. So often one has to accept another's poor plan, since he will not use a good one, then find a way to alter it so that the results may not be as bad as with the original plan. This is called "the better substitute for the worst."

A sense of humor is obviously invaluable. This trait is found in those who do not take life—and more particularly themselves—too seriously. A sense of humor is the balm, the ever-ready healing lotion to be carried by everyone and used on many occasions. Look for the funny elements in everyday living, enjoy the humorous actions of so-called great people, realizing that the world may respect a person for his wisdom but love him for the well-meaning, foolish things he does. Do not be ashamed of making a fool of yourself occasionally; by so doing you demonstrate that you belong to a large and constantly growing fraternity, The Human Race. So make the best of it and help others to enjoy life by constantly accenting its amusing side. A funny story or a humorous twist is frequently all that makes an experience bearable. Try handling a difficult situation with a light touch, as a temporary predicament or inconvenience, not as a crisis. Take the attitude that there is always a way and—what is more—a simple, satisfactory way to deal with all situations. Most people look on trouble as tragedy, when it is merely a hill for strong legs to climb, frequently reaching an unexpectedly beautiful view of life. When climbing an emotional mountain, boost yourself up with a light touch and remind yourself that you are nearing the summit; it is not much farther to the top.

Optimism is always a justifiable virtue. One does not deny unfortunate facts and situations, but having seen them and admitted their unpleasant presence, one should *choose* to see the good aspects and meaning of life. Optimism is constructive; it encourages the flagging spirit to one more effort, and yet one more, until success wipes out all memory of hardship. Optimism is contagious, spreading its reviving power to all it touches; it is truth in the making. The optimistic person is a joy to others, so think optimistically. Be cheerful and encouraging. Make yourself *try;* even if you may not attain exactly what you started for, you will reach a destination in which you will find satisfaction. While you are proceeding towards this goal, keep yourself occupied and hopeful. A purpose in life and the attainment of some degree of success, aided by optimism, will stimulate you to further effort and objectivity.

Poise and calmness do much to help yourself and other people. They are contagious emotions which act like oil on troubled waters. Poise is the result of refusing to be ruffled, of avoiding emotional orgies, of putting first things first—which enables you to remain calm, composed, and able to use good judgment in any emergency. Poise can be cultivated daily, at work, at play, and in the midst of your own family. In handling the small, disconcerting things of life, remember that a well-poised person is never in a hurry to act or speak, is never flustered. A calm, well-poised person might be compared to a sailboat, well-weighted by a deep keel which quickly rights it when it heels over in a gusty wind. The best psychological keel you can have is the belief that God's hand is always on your shoulder, guiding you through shoals and darkness into a safe harbor where a good sailor may head into the wind and ride out the storm.

An adventurous spirit is a necessary part of your correct mental equipment. You must be willing to take chances with your own life if you would help others or progress yourself. Life is a gamble; there is little certainty in it, but one can be careful not to play with stacked cards. Let

"I dare" be your motto. Live with this thought: "I dare to try when something worthwhile may be accomplished for others or for myself. For such a purpose I dare risk burning my fingers. For something of great value to others, I even dare risk burning their fingers for them. I do not take my orders from fear. I shall live fully and completely, knowing that life can be a glorious adventure—if only I dare intelligently and in keeping with my ideals."

The well-adjusted person is a *practical idealist*. He believes in and serves others without thought of reward or recognition. His one purpose is *unself-seeking service efficiently rendered*.

III

The Education of Self

A GENERAL education, unfortunately, seldom includes instruction in the techniques of personal mental hygiene—an omission which accounts for much unnecessary suffering and many failures in life. This lack of public knowledge and training cannot, of course, be entirely rectified by any book on the subject, but it is my purpose to give here some truths, techniques and principles which can be of assistance to anyone who is interested in helping himself or others with emotional problems. And it is hoped that an aroused interest may lead him to go on seeking further knowledge of personal mental hygiene.

Begin self-education by resolving to *use intelligence*, applying it to your own problems and to those of others who may need your help. Most people have sufficient potential intelligence to do a good job in life, but frequently their actions are foolish because they have allowed inertia, ignorance, carelessness or emotional bias to dictate the course of their actions. Many people waste four-fifths of their potential intelligence. Relatively dull people who use their intelligence to the utmost are sometimes more successful than brilliant ones who fail to train and use their intelligence—man's greatest asset. This is how Webster defines intelligence: "The power of meeting any situation, especially a novel situation, successfully by proper behavior adjustments; also, the ability to apprehend the interrelationships of presented facts in such a way as to guide action towards a desired goal." In the light of this definition, how consistently do you think you use your intelligence?

To be happy and successful you must be willing when occasion demands to be uncomfortable intellectually, physically and emotionally. No worthwhile life is easy, although the intelligent person can find and maintain relative comfort. Since intelligence, like muscle, must be exercised if it is to be ready for use when needed, learn to think, to study, to gather and correlate facts in all spheres of life. To be intelligent, be willing to work, to study and to think until your head aches. Thinking is not easy; indeed, the chief reason people do not think is that thinking is too much work. Frequently it means assuming responsibility that they would rather sidestep. It seems much easier to feel than to think, to guess than to know. Often when people try to think, they meet with failure, merely because they have not learned how to think. The use of intelligence is a skill which must be mastered just like tennis, skiing or golf, and as any athlete knows, skills must be maintained by constant practice. Contrary to popular opinion, thinking does not come naturally, but a person who is willing to work at it can accomplish wonders; one who is not can charge up most of his unhappiness and failures to this fact alone. Perhaps you did not have a good education; many people do not, even though they may possess college degrees. Formal schooling is merely an introduction to education which must be carried on daily throughout life. You may have to work much of the day, but everyone has some spare time, and at least one-fourth of this can be used for study and serious reading. Perhaps your work seems uninteresting, routine—neither worthwhile nor productive, since all work sometimes seems that way. But people who have trained their intelligence and accumulated stimulating facts and interests have valuable resources unknown to those who fritter away too many of the rare hours in life by watching ball games, dancing in night clubs, reading detective stories and constant moviegoing. All these amusements have their place. But don't let them take *all* your spare hours. The world belongs, and always will belong, to those who use intelligence. Those who do this unselfishly come near to knowing all the joys of human existence. Value your intelligence! It is adequate to meet all your needs; use it and respect it.

Learn to make definite, well-considered, clean-cut decisions. Know your own mind. Seek and listen to counsel, weigh it carefully and decide for yourself; having decided, abide by your decision. Certainly, sometimes the decision will be wrong, but even so it may work out very well. If you make no decision, you are like a sailboat in stays; it does not answer to the tiller, drifts, and is in danger of being swamped or cast on the rocks If, to reach your decision, you lack necessary information, get it. If you are still undecided but must make a decision, flip a coin and take a chance. Life belongs to the active people who decide on a course and follow it persistently. Only if you discover that your decision was undeniably and hopelessly wrong should you abandon it and make a new one. A decision is not a vow, but it is a definite course of direction. You may not get exactly what you want or expect—as a matter of fact, you seldom will—but you will get something, and it will be far better than the pain of indecision.

It is necessary to be a ready adapter. When it is called for, decide that you *can* fit into any situation, adjust to any person, live in any part of the world, under any circumstances. You may not want to do certain of these things, but that is of little importance if they lie in the path of your objective. When you have made up your mind that you can get along anywhere, under any conditions, you will enjoy using the correct techniques, take pride in being able to adjust immediately, skillfully and gracefully. Only good adapters have any chance of being useful, well and happy people. The fundamental patterns of society and of personal relationships form today a kaleidoscope which changes with increasing rapidity; only quick, expert adaptation enables one to be unhurt by the demands of rapid changes.

Adaptation involves no sacrifice of principles, but it does necessitate consideration of the principles of others and frequent compromises. In personal relationships two intelligent people are bound to disagree sometimes, but in their disagreement they will always have a common meeting place in their mutual respect. To become a good adapter: first, realize that personal adaptation is an absolute necessity; second, decide that it will be your way of life, and then proceed to train yourself in the art of adapting. Accept the people you live with; stop trying to change and improve them; attempt to understand them and anticipate their actions. Adapt to those you work with, understand them, see what they are trying to do. Rule out all anger and hatred resulting from your frustration; like your associates, be kind to them. Adjust to the weather, hot or cold, rain or shine; do not let it interfere with your plans, but merely change your way of carrying out your plans. Associate with people in all strata of life, rich and poor, educated and uneducated, good and bad, cultivated and uncultivated. In a full life you will meet pro-communists and anti-communists, capitalists and laborites, illiterates and pedants. You do not have to adopt their views, but you should understand them and why they think and feel as they do. Take pride in your ability to get along with all kinds of people, under all sorts of conditions, in any place in the world.

By far the most difficult job is to adapt to one's self. The gap between what we want to be, feel we should be, and think we are often seems unbridgeable—and probably it is. Even so, it is best to strive for high standards of personality. We agree with Browning that "A man's reach should exceed his grasp, or what's a heaven for?" The truth, however, is that many of us would like to be a composite of the one most valuable characteristic that each outstanding man and woman we know possesses. We desire the poise of a great diplomat, the charm of a recent president, the wisdom of a famous financier, the judgment of a noted engineer and the knowledge of a Supreme Court judge. We aspire to all of these talents, but each genius mentioned may have only one such talent himself. Therefore, as a vital part of this self-education process, train yourself to adapt to yourself, to know and like the material with which you must work so that you may use it to the best possible advantage. Make the most of what you have. No one person has many talents; he may, however, take the few he possesses and make them pay enormous dividends. An outstandingly successful man stated—with truth—that his only talent was persistence; that his determination to see things through, never give up, never turn aside, was his greatest single asset.

Being a ready adapter comes more easily to some people than to others. People who seem able to get along with everyone have been reared in an environment which taught adjustment; others have been brought up in insecurity and conflict which created fear and rebellion—the archenemies of adaptation. For most people adaptation is an art, the value of which must first be recognized, and then years of self-training spent in perfecting it. Maladaptation is largely due to the misuse of one's own emotions or the misinterpretation of another's. The better-adjusted person is the one who has mastered the science and art of *directing* the emotional energies of himself and of others.

To accomplish this it is necessary to understand the fundamentals of human instincts.

The ever-increasing complexities of society make it imperative for man to understand and direct intelligently his instinctive emotional drives. Human beings, like most other animals, have strong primitive drives which demand satisfaction. If denied or repressed with intolerance, these inherent drives may give rise to both physical and mental illness. For thousands of years man has used his intelligence to build a civilization which affords him protection, comfort and many rewards—but demands in return that his actions become less and less instinctive in nature. The price of civilization is decreased satisfaction of the primitive instinctive drives, and it is a high price—particularly when the terms of exchange are not understood. Emotions are important factors in the lives of all human beings; indeed, they are the mainspring and furnish the energy for human action. Emotions cannot be denied, but their importance can be magnified or minimized. Emotions should be accepted as a normal part of life, entirely free of ethical connotation. It is not wicked to be angry with one's brother, to be afraid, to feel tenderly toward the wife of another man, but it will probably be very unfortunate if you react to your emotions as your instincts dictate. Remember the axiom: "You are not responsible for your emotions, but you are accountable for your actions."

You must learn to assess the value of emotion; recognize it when it intrudes, but realize that it is not a reliable guide to conduct—it may cause you to do something stupid or destructive. As an intelligent person, you have a choice as to how you will comply with your emotions: you need not be their slaves; on the contrary, if you will keep the mastery they will furnish the energy for intelligent and idealistic conduct.

People develop patterns of behavior at an early age, which is another way of saying that life is largely a matter of habits—habits of thought, of feeling and of action. Since this is true, it behooves us to develop good, useful, dependable, constructive habits. The nervous system has a definite tendency to repetition; once we have thought, felt, or acted in a certain way, we are more likely to repeat that process than to develop a new one. It is as if channels were made in the mind, with mental energy flowing through them, cutting them ever deeper through use until only a flood of emotion or intellectual inspiration can cause new mental channels to be evolved.

Each individual deepens his own channels, develops his own patterns of acting, feeling and thinking. Most of these go back to such an early age that he considers them an integral part of himself, taking his concepts for granted as he does his feet and hands; it seems to him he has always been this way, and that it is the only way to be. He does not realize that he has illogical and mistaken preferences and prejudices acquired from those with whom he associated when he was very young; that his way of moving, his thought processes, the way he feels and reacts to his feelings—indeed, his entire fund of so-called facts—have all been grafted on him, some correctly and some incorrectly, and that on these are based his conception of truth, of right and wrong.

It is imperative that one understand one's own mental patterns, see how they developed, comprehend why one is this way now, and know more or less what one is going to be like tomorrow. Fortune-telling is not difficult if one knows another's life history; regardless of what circumstances the individual is in, he tends to repeat his pattern of conduct, more or less influenced by his environment, but as a rule less. Herein lies the truth that the child is father to the man. Yet there is great hope in this situation. Though one's mental channels are at times blocked by an obstruction, this can be seen and removed. New channels can be cut, and if one knows the course and force of the stream, it is possible to cross at an angle—one need not swim against the current.

Many people are not familiar with any of their mental patterns and do not realize that they repeat themselves daily. They are lost and traveling in a circle. Some people are not willing to see the patterns of their lives, and so have a protective amnesia in regard to their past—an escape technique which is an inadequate device that never really protects.

The first essential in helping yourself is to understand yourself. "You shall know yourself, and the truth will make you free." It will enable you to recognize your most frequent mental patterns. To accomplish this, write an autobiography, putting down, as far as you know, why you did this or that, and you may find in it a useful revelation.

For example: "A" quit college in his third year to work in a bank. After four years in the bank he quit to go into farming. After three years he left the farm to study accounting. After six years of accounting, feeling he was getting nowhere, he quit to accept a position as a minor executive. And so his life history continued; he never stayed long enough on any one job to pass through the period of failure which enables one to enter the portal of success. At the age of forty-five he awoke to this fact, decided to see his next job through, changed some of the patterns of his life and achieved the success he had always desired and had the ability to secure.

Watch the patterns of your conduct with amused tolerance; become better acquainted with yourself, your very funny and yet worthwhile self. Then get busy and form a few new worthwhile patterns. Stand erect; walk as if you are going somewhere; smile; turn on your charm at all times; be energetic; be for things and not against them. Do not try to correct all your patterns of life—use what you have intelligently. If some are destructive, add something to them and neutralize them. Realize that the other person has patterns of conduct of which he is unaware; he probably does not even know they exist. It is wiser to change the course of a stream by cutting a new channel at a place you have chosen than to dam the stream and be swept away when the dam breaks. And remember that it need not, and probably cannot, all be done at once. The perfection of a medieval cathedral took centuries to achieve.

Many life patterns which are destructive have become so as a matter of accident but could have been developed constructively had the effort been made. The development of constructive patterns necessitates the correlation of experience. Nearly everyone has a mass of experience from which he does not trouble to learn. Science has progressed infinitely more through correlation of knowledge than by accidental discovery, and the same is true of the development of character and personality. But with many persons, knowledge is like the scattered pieces of a picture puzzle, which must be fitted together if the various designs of life are to become evident.

The recognition of your patterns of life and the correlation of experience will lead to a reasonable amount of foresight, which is of course necessary to everyone. Foresight will not enable you to know exactly what to expect around the next turn in life, but it does reveal some of the possibilities and help you to take advantage of them, and so avoid serious accidents. The good automobile driver not only sees what is in front of and behind his car, but also prepares for what he may find around the next blind corner; since he is so planning, his car is under control at all times.

If you are going to use foresight, you cannot be a worrier, because foresight is a purely intellectual accomplishment. If you are worrying, your judgment is not to be trusted. It is like playing a guessing game when you are worried; your judgment is so twisted that you cannot possibly guess right. Worry is the bad habit which an apprehensive person has picked up from a close relative or associate in childhood. Worry is stupid, unattractive, painful and perhaps a little cowardly. The "softer" one is the more he worries. The worrier always takes trouble badly, even before it happens. You can avoid that pattern. Make up your mind that you are going to have a certain amount of trouble in your life; there is nothing you can do to avoid it and the only way you can beat the game is to take that trouble in your stride. It is not your trouble that upsets your life but the way in which you take it.

Hurry is another unattractive habit which the person who uses foresight and planning in his life can usually avoid. The only thing one can say about hurry is that it enables you to make more mistakes faster, interferes with poise, destroys grace and obscures the actual values of life. You may be sure that if you do it in a hurry, you will almost always do the wrong thing in the wrong way. But if you really must hurry—hurry skillfully!

Worry and hurry, which are wasters of time and effort, lead us to the consideration of energy. Most people have plenty of energy, if only they would use it correctly. With the exception of those few who suffer from a rare disease, there is almost no one who actually lacks strength and energy. Most of the people who claim or really think they have too little energy have acquired this idea from a mistaken parent or physician, or else it is a subconscious method of avoiding the discomforts of life—for which dubious reward they pay by sacrificing most of the usual joys and happiness of living.

Eliminate any idea that you are weak or that you lack energy. If you believe you lack energy, you are simply misguided. It is not the expenditure of energy which fatigues you; it is not using enough energy and not using it constantly. Fatigue does no one harm but is, instead, the first step toward real strength. Be glad you are tired; perhaps you are getting somewhere at last. Only too frequently to be "rested" means to be "arrested." The well-adjusted person makes the effort for both the small and the big things; he tries, tries and tries, laughing while he does it, though perhaps tears may be induced by temporary discomfort. He counts on his mental second wind, never acknowledging permanent defeat because while he is alive he can always keep trying. Frustration is of no importance; it is merely a signal for reorientation as to direction and method. Of course you are going to do what you set out to do, or something like it, but you may need to correct your technique, and frustration is the warning signal that tells you so.

Life is largely a matter of self-education; of self-discipline, not through inhibitions and repressions, but as a result of exercising your greatest asset—the power of choice. Learn to use the words "either—or"; to choose that which you want most. Having chosen, devote your life emotionally, intelligently and spiritually to attaining that choice. When you have attained it, what is it worth? Something of value—to give to someone else. For the choice of the highest is merely cutting a channel that your best may flow through yourself to others.

IV

First Aid for the Adult

No one ever became an adult overnight, nor did he inherit intact a wholesome, well-integrated personality. It takes hard, honest plugging to be as adult in *mind* as you are in *years*—to be able to think, act and feel on a mature level. But you can become truly mature by developing the correct techniques. And what a joy it is to be, or to live with, a really adult person!

What are the minimum psychological requirements for maturity? These characteristics are perhaps the most important:

1. The ability to use your intelligence objectively.
2. A willingness to face facts on all occasions.
3. An avoidance of rationalization—that is not letting your emotions sway your intelligence.
4. A good understanding of the everyday knowledge and principles influencing your social milieu, and acceptance of them.
5. A comprehension of the nature of instinct.
6. Minimizing the "pleasure-pain" motif of life, and placing wise action ahead of comfort or discomfort.

7. Complete emotional emancipation from parents and the attainment of a reasonable amount of independence.

8. Belief in a God to whose laws you try to conform.

9. Belief in the brotherhood of man.

10. Contribution of service to the community.

These are only the minimum requirements. To be an adult you should also:

Avoid the projection of failures on others.

Refrain from adverse criticism.

Be *for* things and not against them.

Be reasonably energetic.

Be ambitious, but not at the expense of others.

Be eager to share success with others.

Be free of jealousy, envy, self-pity, suspicion and vengefulness.

To achieve the goal of becoming adult in thinking, feeling, and acting it may help to consider the handicaps others have overcome in attaining this end. Nearly all persons are to a certain extent handicapped by some childish emotional reaction, prejudice, habit or misconception. These are psychological blind spots, which exist even though most people do not know what they are. The discovery of such a blind spot is resented by nearly everyone, since his habitual reactions have mistakenly become more or less sacred to him; his attitude is, "Right or wrong, this is the way I am." This is only a way of fooling yourself.

It is *not* the way you are; it is the erroneous conception or label which your early associates pasted on. Children can get by with such erroneous conceptions, but grownups no longer can. An adult has the ability to reverse himself if need be; to grant that he has been entirely mistaken, to endure the temporary discouragement of having a blind spot revealed. Only by recognizing the blind spots can they be eliminated.

Every human being has a number of psychological blind spots, and they are all foci which cause continuous serious maladjustment. These are so serious and often ugly that each person walls them off from his conscious mind. Other people are somewhat aware of them, but they dislike to tell him about them because they usually care for him and are ashamed for him, and they know, too, that he will probably hate them if they help him to such necessary self-revelations.

Many adults are only adolescents grown physically older, inasmuch as they are still sentimental, emotional, excitement-seeking, pleasure-loving, dependent but blustering individuals who hope they can get something for nothing, or at least for bargain prices. But this need not be so. I know one woman who remained an adolescent until she was fifty-four years old. Then she dispensed with the unsatisfying pleasure of playing with her adolescent psychological dolls and took on the more rewarding and far more interesting responsibilities of adult reality.

Work is purposeful activity and is the integrating force in society. A task, whether set by others or by one's self, gives continuity of purpose to activity, prevents expensive and boring dawdling, forces the matching of mental images with reality, and gives a person the satisfaction of accomplishment. People can never be happy, well and prosperous unless they work gainfully or for inner contentment the greater part of the day. The demand for less work and more free time, if carried to extremes, can rot the structure of civilization and undermine the character of man. People must have good, hard work; work in which they can develop their abilities and character, and work for which they are well paid, either in cold cash or true satisfaction. Not less work, but more work for more pay, for the more abundant life, and more to share with others.

A good workman respects himself and his job; only by believing in himself because of his accomplishment can he come to believe in his fellow men. Work is practically man's only method of orientating himself constructively and happily to other human beings. One of the greatest joys in life is learning how to do something a little better. Work in itself is among the finest things in life, but man makes it unpleasant if he assumes an erroneous attitude toward it. If a law were passed making any form of work illegal, people would soon be on their knees begging for it, willing to pay to be allowed to work, even bootlegging it. Mature adults look upon work as a great privilege and not as a punishment. When God drove Adam and Eve out of the Garden of Eden and told them they must earn their living by the sweat of their brow, he conferred not a curse but a blessing on them. At last they had something to do to decrease their boredom with one another; they could enjoy the pleasure of resting after honest toil, could see the results of their work and could know they were no longer parasites on God's bounty.

Many business employees are dissatisfied with their work because of inopportune timing. The timing element is important in every organization. It may be that certain opportunities will not occur at a time when they can be taken advantage of. On the other hand, tempting holes occasionally appear in many organizations, and then a far-sighted person wins more than his just reward. One has to time one's efforts; many people fail to do this, and so blame others or life for their lack of success.

In order to do good work a person must know what it is he is trying to accomplish; he must learn to get along with fellow workers, cooperate one hundred per cent and adjust to the vagaries of others. Take the attitude that you belong to a theatrical stock company. The other actors are all temperamental and unreasonable, but you accept them as they are. Since you are determined that the group shall put on a good show, you help them in every possible way, make them feel as important as possible; then when your time comes to step on the stage, you will make the most of it. Ignore the faults of your associates, forgive their errors, try not to see their failures. These faults, errors and failures are of little importance—except to cite mistakenly as a justification for your own faults, errors and failures. Find your associate's best point, play it up all the time—that is the talent he has; use it! You do not berate a jackass because he does not sing in grand opera, but pet and praise him as he helps carry a heavy burden up a steep mountain, even though he does this slowly.

Learn to get along with people with a smile, praise, a good word for everyone.

Learn to get along not only with your fellow workers but with the boss. If you criticize the boss, it merely marks you as a small person. Certainly the boss does wrong—who does not? The boss is not a perfect person, but he is probably someone who can calmly endure more trouble than the next person, and still keep his head. Also he is the logical whipping boy for every employee. There are three types of bosses: First, those who try to help one find and employ one's abilities, who realize a junior must be trained, disciplined and prepared for responsibilities. These make up by far the largest group, since they know how hard it is to find an able employee, and are constantly trying to develop one. The second is the too-pleasant boss. He seldom crosses you, praises you indiscriminately, once in a while gives you a small raise, and allows you to hope for much more. You love him, never realizing that the pleasant boss who does not expect much of you is probably your greatest enemy. Third, there is the unfair, hard boss. Do not worry about him; do not bother to get angry with him. If he is what you think he is, he will soon break and be out of the way. Why not prepare yourself for his job? It will be vacant soon!

Leadership. The understanding worker who has through understanding and experience become skilled in helping people in trouble will find that in times of crisis this ability will prove of even greater service. Almost instinctively a group recognizes the qualities of personality necessary to meet difficult situations that must be dealt with promptly and efficiently. Spontaneously they turn for leadership to one who has demonstrated competence in solving similar problems, and who can inspire others to work together harmoniously.

To be chosen as leader is not merely a flattering honor but a serious obligation to assume responsibilities that one has been judged capable of fulfilling. A "boss" or dictator may for a time arrogate to himself a position of authority, but he is never chosen as a leader, and sooner or later he finds himself without followers. Often, in fact, the group that at first seemed to accept his authority turn against him, and seek for themselves a leader with whom they willingly cooperate to attain a desired objective.

Although leaders may vary greatly in personality, there are certain attributes which make for successful leadership. Fortunately these qualities may be cultivated and from a minimum endowment be developed to a high degree.

Effective leadership must come from a person who is above all an emotionally mature adult. He must be able to see objectively, to think clearly and to act wisely. Discarding handicapping emotions, he must be able to exercise good judgment, strengthened through the daily practice of making clear-cut decisions, then acting upon them without delay or post-mortem regrets.

The mature leader is a fully integrated, well-balanced

adult, sincere, self-respecting and social-minded. Conscious of his own worth, he recognizes that of others and accords appreciation and respect for personality similar to that which he receives from them. A "boss" demands recognition; a leader earns the respect and allegiance of the other members of the group.

The leader regards himself as one of the team, leading but not "starring." By virtue of his position, he must observe, evaluate and assign to each member of the team the part which he is best fitted to play. He then encourages each player to do his best; inspires him with the confidence that makes for the success of the team. The leader must make a fine discrimination between the "rights" of the individual players and the main objective of the team as a whole—the accomplishment of a purposive goal. Regardless of personal feeling, the leader's decision must always be for the good of the whole group, even though this may sometimes be at the sacrifice of an individual player.

True leadership is free from jealousy. The leader must recognize some abilities in certain players which are superior to his own. The good of the team is served when he helps that player develop his special gift to the utmost. The recognition accorded the fortunate player encourages other members of the team to believe that they, too, may have talents which will be equally valued, inspires each man to do his best.

The mature leader understands both himself and the members of his team. Through study and experience he has gained a dependable store of knowledge of human behavior, of the motivations underlying the actions of individuals and groups. He realizes that inadequate knowledge, false conceptions and ill-defined objectives may lead to lack of cooperation on the part of an individual, even antagonism of a minority group who may defeat the accomplishment of the goal the majority wish to attain. He does not offer uncompromising opposition, nor assert his authority, but instead he invites the minority to free and open discussion. Patient, tolerant listening, together with acceptance of any feasible suggestions offered, leads to an honest meeting of minds, and most often results in cooperation from a former pressure group that might have become disrupting.

One of the greatest of military men who was ever in supreme command, Field Marshal Foch, expressed ably his concept of leadership: *

"I have not so much sought to command, as to lead those associated with me to share my ideas—which is quite different. Often I was in a position to give formal orders, categorically; but this is not my way. And I know that when one obeys contrary to his own convictions, he obeys badly. I preferred to convince each one that my plan was perfectly feasible, and I endeavored to inspire each with the desire to attain it. What is truly worthwhile is to understand those with whom we are working and have them understand us. To understand fully is the whole secret of life."

The man who gets into a management role must be a person who can think functionally and who can think in comprehensive, broad, over-all terms. His specialty is man-

* From editorial in "Le Matin," Paris, 14 Avril 1930

agement—not sales, accounting, engineering or actuarial science. He chooses persons with "know-how" in special fields. He confers with them. He builds the ball team. He chooses and develops those who will play particular roles on that team, but he is not the player. He is a coach who sees every game and how well it is played. From time to time he makes suggestions for improvement in individual role playing which he himself might not be able to achieve but which he is sure the individual with whom he is working has the potential to achieve.

The manager must be creative, imaginative, always looking for new experiences. His time is not consumed with minor details. He thinks about company policy, philosophy, and objectives. He constantly asks toward what end and for what purpose his company exists.

The successful manager is also a spiritual, philosophical leader. He is not a gadgeteer or a specialist in technique, except in the technique of interpersonal relations and administration.

The expert manager is not status-conscious. He does not need to demand respect; he earns it. He moves to and fro within his company, inspiring here, analyzing there, encouraging a trend, curbing a trend, and withal is a human leader. He is no longer competitive—he is cooperative. He is both a scientist and an artist.

The manager, be he president or supervisor, must be a well-balanced individual. He is not easily swayed from the major and immediate goals of his company. He may listen here and there to tremendous arguments and fantastic schemes of his executive group. However, under pressure he is steady, deliberate, patient, creative and genuine. At the same time he is firm, calm, direct, positive and balanced. He controls his anger and his elation. Where these qualities are lacking, there we find perforations in management.

The leader understands himself. He understands his frustrations, blind spots, motives and goals. He understands others. He knows what makes them tick. He understands *why* people behave the way they do.

The professional manager understands why pressure groups, too, behave the way they do. He understands what persons as well as groups are trying to achieve through their behavior, be it oblique, antagonistic or cooperative. He does not easily get caught in the surface generalizations of a situation. He asks questions. He continues to ask questions. He seeks deep in under the surface to discover what is going on in the thinking and attitude of his staff.

The lonely, egocentric, selfish, inhibited, frustrated, low-ability manager is usually a big problem in any organization. The spirit and tone of an organization is an elongation of the spirit and tone of its top management. Management sets the pace. What is found down the line in an organization in quality, attitude, outlook, ability, understanding and balance is found first in its leadership.

One of the most difficult things to achieve in professional management is the ability to detach oneself more and more from operations and to apply oneself more and more to the development and growth of individuals. This means the ability and disposition to delegate responsibility —grave and heavy responsibility—which often the manager in his loneliness feels no one else can handle.

The manager must bring out of confused organization clear lines of responsibility, with individuals clearly assigned to those responsibilities. His job becomes one of working himself out of the job. His role is one of power *with* people, not power *over* people. He often is a lonely man—left to his own counsel and ingenuity. He often needs professional counsel outside the organization.

Avoid crises as if they were the atomic bomb. Try to advance from job to job with the liking and respect of all associates. The trouble a person has with associates is due not to them but to himself. Nothing is truer than the saying that one carries his own troubles within himself. A change of environment seldom changes the nature of a person's difficulties. Frequently these are the result of inner dissatisfactions which are in no way related to work. These dissatisfactions should be solved in the area where they belong—within yourself—and not brought to work, any more than the problems related to the job should be carried into home and social life.

Next to a person's inner resources, first-class friends are his greatest asset. Conversely, second-class friends are the greatest liability. Know as many people as possible, and know them as well as possible. Tell acquaintances little about yourself or your ideas; get them to talk about themselves, and they will love you. Promise acquaintances nothing, but among them constantly look for a new friend, a truly first-class person, one who has the courage to criticize, to demand your best self, a person who has different interests and different beliefs from yours, a friend for whom you can render a constructive service. A friend is not one who does something for you but is a person who is kind enough to let you do something for him. Devote energy toward making such friends. Retain them, never let them go, and continue making new friends until you die.

Marriage is usually looked upon as an adult's greatest joy, but only too often it is also his greatest problem, largely because of ignorance, handicapping sentiment and natural but unfortunate motivation. Many men marry because of a strong sex drive. Or they look for someone to mother them, though they seldom get it. To a large extent they feel cheated. After a few years of marriage, the wife, who was formerly a playmate, is taken away from her husband by the constant demands of children. These men, disappointed, confused and depressed, turn to their work. A woman may marry for love or for any of a number of other reasons—a desire to be independent, to do the correct social thing, to have someone to support and protect her, to establish a place in society, to have children, and for the companionship of a man who will act as a father—praise her and never be critical of her. Both men and women often have a picture of marriage as it exists only in fairy tales; this they blandly pass on to their children with the same smile on their faces as when telling them about Santa Claus.

But a truly adult person knows that marriage is a hard

reality! Each individual might almost be said to be placed in the jail of the other person—the jail of ideas, feelings, preferences and prejudices—and in this jail he may be bound, frustrated and tempested. In truth it may be said that, by its very nature, marriage is sure to be both a rewarding and a painful experience. It takes a mature mind to realize that the chief purpose of marriage is to offer an unlimited opportunity for service to others without expectation of appreciation or reward. That's why it should not be undertaken when people are too young; not "entered into unadvisedly or lightly, but reverently, discreetly, advisedly, soberly and in the fear of God."

Young people should have had time to mature, to get along in the world away from parents, before attempting to work in double harness. They need to establish themselves, or to make a beginning of establishing themselves, materially before marriage. Wives should bring their husbands a dowry of friends, interests, homemaking skills, culture and knowledge. Husbands should help expand this dowry and be able to support their wives and the coming children on something like a reasonable basis. The fact that boys and girls are willing to marry without these minimum safeguards does not lessen the responsibility of either. Remember always that the secret of a successful marriage is to ask from it nothing except the opportunity to make the other person happy and significant; to do everything one can to love the person to whom one is married. It is not easy; love is a delicate flower which has to be cultivated and protected. Your own love is all you ever really have—but if you have that you are rich!

Husbands and wives get along better when they learn never to step on one another's mental corns; when they learn where these are and keep off them. It also helps when they try never to get angry at the same time; to be kind under all circumstances; to show to each other at least the courtesy they show to strangers; and to refuse to engage in civil war. Marriage can then become a spiritual relationship, made so by years of affectionate association, motivated by unselfishness and mutual consideration.

Children play a large part in the lives of married couples. They bring them unequaled compensations, but at the same time they create problems, many of them unnecessary. In general, fathers would love their children better and would have much more to contribute to them if the mothers were not frequently more possessive than they realize. Many wives take the children away from their husbands, and then blame their husbands (sometimes in the presence of the children) for not being interested in their sons and daughters. Other wives use the children as a means of disciplining their husbands. Many women make outrageous demands for their children—in the name of love! This continues long after the children are grown and sometimes extends even to the grandchildren.

Husbands and wives should allow one another to share in their children, to enter into their lives as they wish; there should be no demand from either as to how the other shall do this. Neither parent should employ children as a sublimation for his own emotional frustration in any sphere. When children are grown, parents should send them out into the world, leave them alone and be big enough to let the children make lives of their own, instead of living vicariously through their children.

Although in most of the emotional problems of marriage friends can only "stand by," not withdrawing friendship from either member of the couple, and not taking sides, they should not feel that they are useless. Friendship is sustaining, and often after the storm blows over each of the two will be grateful.

Finances are a common source of trouble both in and out of marriage. Sometimes a mature friend with practical experience may be able to help others work out for themselves a philosophy in regard to the use of money. Adults should have a proper respect for and ability to use money, understanding money as merely so many hours, days and months of life—a unit of exchange for human energy, physical and mental. Money accrues as a result of our own energy or that of someone else; and it purchases the energy of others. It is, therefore, not to be thrown away or used foolishly but to buy the things one truly wants. A mature person uses money well, just as he does the other tools at his disposal. He does without and skillfully saves in order that he may have the pleasure of helping others. The immature person may have plenty of money, but he knows so little about using it intelligently, that he wastes it on unimportant things. An extravagant or money-careless person is always a selfish one.

A self-regimented way of life is a necessity for all adults. For a balanced life *work, rest, exercise and play* are essential. They must, however, be differently proportioned at the various stages of life. For example, one needs more play in childhood and old age; more work in middle life. These six words, if followed, will do much to help you and every adult:

"*Work, rest, exercise, play—every day.*"

It is not easy to plan and maintain a balanced life, but with determination and the realization that you can in this way attain your greatest efficiency and usefulness, you can do it!

All people need hobbies, vacations, intellectual interests and opportunities for cultural growth. The best use of "spare time" is to enable a person to develop every side of his personality. Leisure in itself is a risk and usually a curse to those people who have no way of using it except in empty pleasures. Is there really such a thing as "spare time"? Start now filling every hour not pledged to work, exercise or rest with play on an adult level. Develop several hobbies; acquire more education; learn to enjoy cultural and aesthetic values. Above all, take vacations! Vacations are not vacuums, as many people think; they are active periods of exercise, travel, seeing old friends and making new ones, developing a hobby or pursuing a new interest—even writing a book or painting a picture.

Adults are likely to be lonely. Learn to allay loneliness for others and to endure it for yourself. Give your companionship without stint; dilute the loneliness of others and you will have less yourself.

Some adults grow sour, irritable and cynical. This usually indicates that they are deeply frustrated and are angry about it, much as a child would be. They are so miserable themselves that they seem to enjoy making others unhappy. An individual who has developed such habits of feeling and thinking not only cannot help others but may be ruining his life. If you are in this state of mind, go to a competent psychiatrist, lay your cards on the table and get help. Once the mote of discontent is removed from your eye, life will be infinitely happier for you—and for everyone with whom you come in contact.

Decide not to be at the mercy of your moods. You do not need to be! Moody people are the ones who self-indulgently allow themselves to be so. Depressed? No interest? Everything an effort? Down? Unhappy? So are we all, at times! What of it? Make the effort; do for others. Moods are of no importance. Make up your mind that you will find something to be happy about, no matter how miserable you feel. Any intelligent person who does not indulge in self-pity can work himself out of a black mood in fifteen minutes.

Just as a ship navigates by degrees of latitude and longitude, so an adult must be aware of and operate on degrees of purpose and ideals. No one can tell another what these should be. Everyone can, however, ascertain which seem to be the most dependable purposes and ideals, bringing greatest usefulness and happiness, by studying those of other happy and successful people.

There is truth in the old axiom that to be fit for life one must learn not to fear death. It should be added that equally one must not fear living. Make up your mind to live fully, courageously, daringly, gracefully, wisely and unselfishly; then you will discover that life is not an ordeal but a glorious adventure.

V

First Aid for Older People

As you reach the later years of your life you can savor innumerable rewards and satisfactions by cultivating the right mental attitudes—by holding fast to the belief, with Browning, that "the best is yet to be, the last of life for which the first was made." There are definite techniques which, if followed wisely, will help you to a rich and happy old age. A careful reading of this chapter should make it easier for you to help yourself, or any older person in your household, to become the kind of adult human being everyone wants most to be.

To generalize about older people is difficult, because in the two extremes of life, childhood and old age, differences, both physical and psychological, are exaggerated. Remember that there is no such thing as a typical old person. Aging is a result of inheritance, the way people have lived, the physical diseases they have had, their attitudes and philosophy about life and society, the environment, and the physiological aging process in itself. Most people, like old cars, have more use left in them than they know—particularly if they have not driven too fast or carelessly, and do not continue to try to speed up. Contrary to general belief, many people have done some of their most valuable work after the age of fifty or sixty; examples are so numerous that you will readily find them yourself. We know others who are going strong throughout their seventies and eighties, frequently putting younger people to shame by their ability to enjoy life, take care of themselves and turn out a neat job.

As you grow older, sooner or later you must expect certain minor handicaps, or as our veterans say, "accept slight disabilities without allowing them to become handicaps." You are not as elastic as you once were. A used rubber band, you know, if stretched, does not come back as fast or as well. Older people neither think nor move quite so quickly, so they must not hurry or be placed under pressure. To a certain extent their physical strength is less; they tire more easily and are more affected by fatigue. Many of the psychological difficulties of older people are the result of fatigue: first, because they do not keep physically fit; second, because they overdo, then become irritable and even emotionally ill. Physical strength is the greatest asset of youth, while the assets of old age are knowledge, experience and skill. Thus, those whose work is largely physical age more quickly than those whose activities are mental.

Fundamentally, your desires as you grow older are the same as those of everyone else—to be of importance and so retain self-confidence, to merit the respect of others, and to have opportunity to employ your energies. The desire to be of importance must be exercised differently in youth and old age: youth can afford to wait, while age must find small ways to be useful each day. Young people try to be self-important, but their wiser elders learn how to be important to others. Their instincts and emotions do not drive them as hard as when they were younger. The great exception to this is fear, which, unfortunately, often seems to increase with age, especially in the basically apprehensive person. Irritability and emotionalism seem nearer the surface and are more easily aroused, but if ignored they quickly subside. Older people recognize this tendency and do not like themselves for it.

It has been said that most people should try some new line of endeavor around the age of fifty-five. By that time they have probably attained their maximum success in the lifework undertaken in youth, and such activity may not now be so urgently necessary for them; families are grown and are no longer as great a responsibility. When, in these circumstances, they continue in the same work they frequently become bored and are merely "trouble shooters" with little of the reward of adventure. New undertakings are salutary, and even if it is not practical to follow this suggestion completely, life will become richer for you as you relinquish some of the routine and details of your former work, and add different things, perhaps allied activities, to your major occupation. The physician who has written medical papers might well become an editor for a medical journal. A broker interested in securities might become an economic counselor; an advertising man turn to merchandising. A homemaker whose responsibilities have lessened as children have married and made homes of their own has more time to devote to gardening and might become an authority in some specialized branch of horticulture, which has always interested her. But whatever the new interest and activity, it should be something which brings you into contact with other people, since older people, especially, are apt to be lonely unless they continue to find opportunities to make new friends.

Such characteristics of age as slowing down physically, a poorer memory for recent events and a tendency to fatigue more easily cannot be prevented. These are, however, frequently little more than minor annoyances to which you can easily adjust and thus avoid becoming a nuisance to yourself or your associates. The psychological difficulties of age are frequently exaggerations of tendencies which existed in youth and were of necessity held in check. Untidy adolescents are likely to grow into older people who are careless of personal appearance; irritable people develop uncontrollable outbursts of rage (sometimes to the point of mental illness); apprehensive people become unduly fearful; stingy ones, penurious; bossy ones, dictatorial. Hypochondriacs have their attention fixed on aches and pains, and the chronically dissatisfied become depressed. The most effective way to become a pleasant, happy and beloved old person is to prepare for it through childhood, youth and middle age—and enjoy life in the process!

Old people are inclined to talk too much; not being able to expend their energy physically, they often do it vocally.

This is exhausting to them and boring to younger people. Because of this garrulousness, which is usually about a period that is finished and is of little interest or importance to contemporary society, old people find that they are avoided. They must learn to be good listeners and not prattle about themselves, their children, their past, their old friends, their former work. When they talk it should be about things they are doing now and which they can make interesting to the person with whom they are talking.

Older people—particularly husbands and wives—are likely to squabble among themselves. Aggressiveness is a male characteristic and submissiveness a female characteristic throughout the animal world. Coincident with passing the sexual climacteric, this changes. As men become less virile their aggressiveness declines; as women become less feminine they become less submissive and more aggressive. If both husband and wife live to a ripe old age the tendency to squabble is increased. He can no longer make her behave as he wishes; and (since he no longer has sufficient power to defend himself against her) the wife has a chance to get even for many things he did when he was younger, things which she inwardly resented but which she could not effectively prevent at the time. Married people should decide long before they reach declining years that they will try never to squabble, bicker, complain, or disagree on any major matter; on the minor ones they will agree to disagree in peace—and it is to be hoped in silence! Habitual quarreling between old people is an ugly sight for others, and, what is more, it poisons their own lives. If they cannot stop it, they should live away from one another. Like the rest of us, many older people need a certain amount of discipline, and, rather surprisingly, they can take it! Like children, they get out of hand because they can get away with it. Many an old person who acts badly and will make no effort to improve his behavior, if faced with the alternatives of being left alone to paddle his own boat or being placed where he can be cared for, would turn over a new leaf and become quite a desirable person in the family group.

One of the greatest joys in life is doing things for yourself, being able to take care of yourself. Busy people who have many responsibilities may have to employ assistants, secretaries and servants to help them, but older people who have fewer responsibilities can derive great satisfaction from looking after themselves. Women can make their own beds, clean and arrange their own bedrooms and bathrooms, take perfect care of their clothes and shoes; and men could do likewise. You should not wait until later years to learn to take care of yourself and your belongings; you should not ask others to do for you the things you can do for yourself. If you train yourself to be less forgetful, careless or self-indulgent, you will make it easier for yourself to live with others. Old dogs can and do learn new tricks, and many an older person somewhat spoiled in youth has decided it is much better to turn over a new leaf and learn to care for himself efficiently!

Older people should always try to be spotless, attractive,

pleasant, and gracious. They need new and currently fashionable clothes, but in a becoming style and appropriate to their physical status, and they must keep these in perfect condition. Most men of seventy are unattractive in shorts, loud sport shirts, or faded, ragged old clothes, without coats; and the same is true of women of that age in slacks or revealing décolleté evening dresses and messy hair. Old people who choose their clothes thoughtfully and keep themselves well groomed are a joy to all with whom they come in contact.

Older people who complain of the manners of the younger generation often have abominable manners themselves. They talk too much, take things for granted, ignore others, expect others to wait on them, decide that they are old enough to do as they please, have bad table manners, and are in other ways outstandingly inconsiderate. Good manners are an older person's most important social asset, and will do much to assure his welcome everywhere. They are largely a matter of being considerate of others, not merely of giving lip service to convention.

As you grow older, more than ever before you need to spend part of each day alone in peace, quiet and meditation; and in prayer that you may be shown how to continue to live each day with courage, kindness, wisdom, laughter, interest and understanding. You should take time to absorb and enjoy the lovely world in which you live and come to know its inhabitants with affectionate amusement. You would do well to budget your time as follows: one-half in work, taking care of personal belongings, etc.; one-fourth in social pastimes with others, both young and old; and one-fourth as an interested, pleased observer of life.

So far in this chapter we have stressed what you should do to help yourself to a rewarding and tranquil old age. Now let us discuss what you can do as a mature adult to help others in your household, or among your friends, to achieve a like result. Because *your* happiness, and that of the rest of your family, may well depend on the wisdom with which you help older people to find *their* happiness.

It is to be hoped that as a young adult you acquired the philosophy of acceptance, and have so perfected it that by the time you are ready to assume the responsibility for helping others it has become part of your nature to accept inevitable difficulties gracefully, without complaint, regret or rebellion. If so, you accept difficulty as you do the weather—frequently, of course, it is not exactly what you would have ordered, but you can "make do with it right well," believing God knows best. With this attitude you will not find it too difficult to help older people.

How, precisely, can a younger adult best help older people? By keeping in mind and following these suggestions:

Do not grant that age interferes with life, but recognize that energy and efficiency vary at different periods throughout life. You need neither deny nor emphasize that they are getting older, but take the general attitude, "You are not as old as you frequently think and sometimes feel."

Try to treat older people as contemporaries; this will be easy if they will do their part.

Give friendly attention, wholeheartedly, affectionately, respectfully and sincerely. You need not spend too much time with them, but go to see them frequently, and give them a heartening dose of enthusiasm, praise, encouragement and even flattery. Tell them something interesting and listen to them for a while. Never be drawn into arguments or disputes. Do not stay too long on one visit.

Encourage older people to do things. Take them a new suggestion or material for something you believe they will like to do (not what you think they *should* do), and give them understanding help to overcome some of the inertia of age so that they will do it. Often your interest and belief that they can do it will be sufficient to get them started, and once started they will carry on. After you get them to work, it is often a good plan to get someone else to go on with them, perhaps a friend of their own age. For example, raising bulbs indoors is not physically tiring, and sharing this hobby with a contemporary may lend added appeal. It will, also, afford older people an opportunity to do something for others, to give to friends or young relatives blooms or potted plants. To be on the giving and not the receiving side keeps up self-esteem. Older women like to go to flower shows, art exhibits, lectures, concerts, the theater, even horse races. They like to dress up and ride in a car for luncheon at different restaurants. Older men enjoy their clubs and may be interested in some small business, or in baseball, football games, parades, political rallies, prize fights and poker games.

Urge older people to have a good time! Often they have a sense of too many responsibilities or worries and too few pleasures. Try to get them to drop their responsibilties and devote more of their lives to having fun. In declining years one may be justified in never letting work interfere with pleasure!

Do not try to change lifelong habits; accept them as they are. Older people do not easily change their daily habits of living; indeed, many people find it hard to do this even in their fifties. Younger people have a tendency to advise older ones that they should make such changes, but this advice is seldom rewarding. It may, in fact, become a source of friction between the old and the young which will lead the older person unconsciously to exaggerate unfortunate habitual reactions. Older people should be encouraged to live each day in their own way.

Do not lightly uproot old people. Try to keep them in an environment with which they are familiar. As people get older they tend to outgrow their homes. Their children are grown and are properly living in homes of their own. The running of a large house, now half-empty, is a burden to the mother and an unnecessarily great expense to the father. Things are run down and worn out, yet Father hates to change, and Mother wants the extra rooms to entice children and grandchildren back, or—as Father looks upon it—to enable her to run a hotel. Beginning around the age of fifty-five many couples wisely start planning to sell out and get a smaller, newer, more modern place. Preparing a home more in keeping with present needs, decorating it, planning a garden, etc., will keep alive interests and homemaking abilities, and make ready a place where one may live should the other die. People should do this while they are still strong and can help one another—but it takes both foresight and courage. Self-indulgent neglect of such wise preparation for the old age that will inevitably come means that most old people have to be uprooted when they are left alone, and this usually causes much unhappiness, even illness. After sixty years of age it is normally hard for most people to adjust to change. Much better help people to face facts before they reach this period, and prepare for a happy, contented old age which they can enjoy.

Help older people to avoid fatigue, not by constantly discussing it or telling them to rest, but by making your own visit short and your outing with them not too long. Ease their physical burden without their knowing that you are doing it. Be tactful in saving their steps, effort and fatigue. Don't let them feel they are a nuisance!

Do not bring them your troubles or allow them to assume your burdens. If you must complain, do it with your contemporaries.

Be gay, light-hearted and friendly. Bring young people to see them. Old ladies particularly like boys, and old men are helped if young girls seem to think that they are still human beings. But if old men want this attention they must learn not to flirt with young girls, or give them "fatherly pats!"

Give older people repeated opportunities to feel useful, but do not make a convenience of them. Do not make a practice of leaving your children with them; do not continually ask them to come and stay with the children; do not use their home as a hotel when you or your children find it convenient. In other words, lean over backwards not to take advantage of older people. Try, however, to find pleasant, constructive opportunities for them to help and to feel important.

Ignore deep-rooted eccentricities and fixed ideas. Do not nag or try to boss them. Give them their freedom and let them use their power of choice, just as you expect to have yours. You may worry about them a bit for fear they will not use that freedom well, but old people took that chance with youth; now you must take a chance with old age!

VI

First Aid for Children

FIRST aid for children, both physical and psychological, is most often rendered by parents, so it is largely to parents that this chapter is addressed. But everyone, even though not a parent, is sometimes called on to act as a friendly guide and support to children. From both the practical and sentimental points of view, this is a challenging and worthwhile undertaking, although if the truth be faced people are more likely to do things for children from an emotional than from an objective motive. Resolve that whatever is done for children shall be not for the adult's pleasure or convenience but for the long-range good of the children. Using foresight and applying intelligence objectively, one can in most instances determine what will be best for a particular child in a specific situation. If one thinks of the principles involved, and not just of the immediate issue, one is less likely to go wrong. When one lacks specific and sufficient knowledge, one can get more. In almost every community there are books on child training that are sound and dependable. If you are called on to make an immediate decision and you feel unsure, risk a "yes" rather than a "no," and in general do the thing which is kind. It may perhaps not be the wiser course, but there is a fifty per cent chance that it will be. At any rate, the child will appreciate your good intention toward him and will be better prepared to accept a positive "no" on an occasion when you have no question as to what is to be done. Never let your decision be based on pride, fear of failure, an exaggerated maternal instinct (mistakenly called love) or possessiveness, which are parental driving sentiments that are not constructive.

From a practical standpoint, a well-reared child is less of a nuisance to himself, more of a joy to the family and a greater potential asset to society than a carelessly brought-up child. Anyone who has owned an obedience-trained dog knows what a wonderful friend he is, and—understanding what is expected of him—how happy the dog is. The same is true of children. They need consistency in treatment, and clearly defined limits to their behavior. So much has been written about not repressing a child, not disciplining it, and so many schools are operated on this approach, that young parents are often confused and almost afraid to use common sense in bringing up their children. Many children brought up in accordance with this new school of psychology are, if possible, less well adjusted to life and more given to emotional illness than were their forebears who were reared under a simpler and sterner, yet more personal and loving, regime. Parents should view new theories with a reasonable amount of skepticism. As we have seen, intricate and complicated theories are usually of no value.

If it were only possible, psychological first aid for children would start with the grandparents' bringing up their children with love, wisdom, understanding and courage, so that these children when they became parents might do likewise for their children. Even so, allowance must be made for biological differences in human beings. A great deal, however, can be accomplished in one generation if parents will adjust their own lives intelligently in order to serve the needs of the child they have brought into the world. While it is true that maladjusted parents are more likely to have maladjusted children, this is not because of any factor of inheritance but is a result of the force of example.

Three of the most important factors that enter into the bringing up of a child are the home, the school and the way other children in the same society are reared. Any one of these can to a large extent undo the work of others. Only by cooperation among the three can really good results be attained. But, to paraphrase St. Paul, "The greatest of these is the home." When the home offers understanding, security and an atmosphere of mutual happiness, children can—and do—manage to graduate from overcrowded, understaffed schools that may even have low academic standards, without serious psychological damage. Although it is sometimes difficult for children to understand why they are not allowed to do what they believe "everybody does," if the home relationships are right, they can accept the parents' decisions with good grace, and enjoy the substitutes which wise fathers and mothers provide in lieu of forbidden pleasures.

Unfortunately, somewhere along the line parents have lost sight of the fact that as taxpayers or patrons of private schools they have a right to express an opinion as to the education they wish the school to give their children. Indeed, this is not merely a right but a parental responsibility. Perhaps parents' attitudes toward schools—or toward some schools which they are more or less compelled to use—is natural in view of the fact that some schools, public and private, consider parents as nuisances. I have known of communities with an unduly large proportion of "problem children," made problems to some extent by the fact that the educational authorities had an inimical attitude toward parents. To encourage cooperation between home and school, parents should take a more active interest in understanding the needs of the schools, and what they as citizens as well as parents can do to help. They should know the teachers with whom their children are associated for so many hours each day, and should be constantly on guard to prevent the child's being exposed to the contagious neurotic attitudes of any maladjusted teacher. While parents should teach children to respect the school's authority, the child is not always in the wrong when he is "in bad" with a teacher. Be sure of the facts, then act intelligently and objectively, but do not allow a child to be unhappy for any length of time over a school situation. (If the situation is one which cannot be remedied, you should in the child's interest transfer him to another school.) You will not, of course, criticize the school unfavorably and so influence the child that he makes no effort to adapt to teacher and schoolmates, but you should let him know that you not only want him to do well in school, but expect him to be happy there. Parents can learn to listen without comment, and can keep open minds as they encourage children to talk freely about their school life; only in this way will they understand and be able to act as mediators between an unhappy or maladjusted child and his school—which may or may not be making life difficult for him. Sometimes it may be that the child is making life difficult for the teacher! Be able to see both sides.

Since children's attitudes are conditioned by those of their parents, the attitudes of parents with whose children yours associate cannot be ignored. Parents should get together and reach some sort of understanding as to how the children in their community will be reared. In the final analysis responsibility for the child's training and character formation all comes back to the home. A good home can carry children successfully through a poor educational atmosphere and an unfortunate social milieu, but more wisdom and greater flexibility are required on the part of the parents, with careful planning for a united program of recreation and social life.

Bringing up children is not a Herculean task, and the problems are, fortunately, spread over the years; crises do not occur all at once. Use common sense, do not expect too much, know when to stop and let the young learn to do for themselves. Many of the difficulties of modern children are the result of having too much or too little done for them; the important thing is to find the middle way. Tackle with confidence the job of rearing your children. Of course you will make mistakes, but if the basic principles are correct your children will do well in spite of your errors of judgment.

(The first principle to remember is that you are dealing with primitive beings, unsocialized, uneducated and motivated by primitive instincts and a need to express energy.) Their actions, thoughts and feelings cannot be accurately interpreted by an adult. There is no difference between the new-born baby of today and an Indian infant of five hundred years ago, except that today's baby has a busy time ahead as society trains it to become a civilized human being. In children we see undisguised expressions of primitive life—anger, fear, sex, shame, pride, jealousy, disgust and curiosity, plus purposeless energy. Although adults have to a certain extent organized and disciplined these same forces within themselves, they are also to a somewhat lesser degree at the mercy of the same unreasoning and illogical drives which they attempt to rationalize.

For the first few years child care is often thought of as largely a matter of physical training: feeding, sleeping, sphincter control, walking and talking. During this time, however, children feel and observe the emotional reactions of the adults around them, and since they are passing through a state of mimicry their own reactions to emotions may be set for life by those of parents and other adults with whom they are closely associated in their limited environment. This is the period when the only communication between children and adults is emotional in nature, and so the attitudes of adults become emotional patterns in children. For example, practically all infants give themselves pleasure by genital manipulation. This is not an acceptable custom, and parents may repress the infant by showing disapproval and disgust—though the parents may not know they are showing disgust. They often slap the child's hand and say, "That is not nice; it is dirty and horrid!" This may well explain why all their lives civilized people feel that sex is "dirty," although intellectually they do not believe it.

Following the first years of training in the home, the child's education is carried on mainly through our social institutions. Since he is still to a large extent an instinctive little animal, education should at first be made as appealing as possible in order that the child be pleasantly conditioned to school. However, the philosophy of free expression—make your work play, do only what interests you—must be replaced by a reasonable discipline that will lead toward self-discipline. A respect for authority will lead toward the ability to direct one's self and others. A voluntary surrender of useless freedom of action, through exercise of the power of choice, will enable one to have true freedoms and lasting rewards. And this reasonable discipline will bring the gradual acceptance of responsibility and the ability to pass through hardship and disappointment without being handicapped by too great suffering. The true purpose of education is not merely the absorption of knowledge, but learning how to think and acquiring facility in associating with people.

In general, we think of the child as having certain fundamental rights or needs which must be met if he is to develop into a useful, happy adult. The seven needs which seem most important are:

1. SECURITY AND PROTECTION

The child should feel secure at all times, not entirely because there is no danger, but from the certainty that his parents can protect him and will teach him how to protect himself. Children need security of a home in which there is love, understanding and friendship between the parents; they should not be made aware of financial or other parental insecurity. Children must be protected from disorganizing and harmful forces in the environment; security and protection are necessary that they may develop unhampered, that they may not at an early age acquire a fear of insecurity. Later every child should be taught to enjoy the challenge of temporary insecurity.

2. FREEDOM

Children are entitled to freedom to grow and develop in accordance with their natures; freedom to take chances, to discover for themselves, to have their own ideas, to learn to trust themselves. The person who truly trusts himself is more likely to trust others. Children are not to be imprisoned in the jail of adult ideas and beliefs, but they are to be shown our mental treasures, the ones we like best and find most useful, and told why we value these intangible possessions that we have gathered through many years.

3. A WISE PARENT SETS A GOOD EXAMPLE

To a considerable extent children model themselves after the parent of the same sex. Boys walk and talk like their fathers, girls dress like their mothers, and so on. Parents should remember that both consciously and unconsciously their children are copying them.

4. COMPANIONABLE PARENTS

Parents who play with their children as if they were children of the same age, who keep alive their own spirit of play and actually enjoy a day on the beach, swimming, playing ball and make-believe, are the ones who can most easily influence, train and educate their children. Although the child wants to feel that he can depend on parental wisdom and authority, upon occasion he needs parents who are companionable, who can come down to his age level naturally and without condescension, who talk, act, think, feel and play as a child does. It is particularly important that the father, who is of necessity away from his children many hours a day, devote at least a few hours every week end to being with his children, following their choice of play. People in their fifties remember as among the happiest hours of their lives Saturday afternoons spent hiking with Father, or having Mother join them for a simple outdoor supper and quiet games in the twilight.

5. PLANNED, CONSISTENT TRAINING FOR LIFE

Parents and educators need a simple, workable plan for carrying out the essentials of their most important responsibility—the training of a child for life. Such a formula includes good habits of everyday living in terms of work, rest, exercise and play; respect for themselves and others, together with the belief that life is equally significant for all; an abiding sense of spiritual values and, reinforcing these, a desire for beauty, the cultivation of courage and a constant dedication to the truth. This plan should be patiently, affectionately and understandingly adhered to.

6. SELF-DISCIPLINE

Parents should keep constantly in mind the fact that self-discipline is the goal of all discipline, and indeed they may well explain this to the child at rather an early age. Children who learn to bathe and dress themselves, not because it relieves Mother of a burden but because it is one of the steps in growing up and becoming independent, have an accepting attitude toward discipline. Toys will be put away joyously, with increased self-respect and a glow of satisfaction at the approval received from the beloved adults who make up a child's small world. Habits learned with pleasure are retained. Conversely, those acquired under the pressure of mere authority are discarded once the child is "free." Discipline can be temporarily imposed, but then it does little good and often sets up a resistance to authority which continues into later school and work relationships. The individual who has gradually learned self-control and self-discipline is more comfortable, more secure, more efficient and happier than the unstable, undisciplined person who really hurts himself more than anyone else.

7. LOVE AND AFFECTION

Love is a child's greatest need. Through his parents' unselfish, mature, demonstrative, happy love he begins to learn the true meaning and abiding joy of love. Seventy per cent of the people in the world do not know the meaning of love, since most of them were not taught it by parents and very few can learn it after they have grown up. Fundamentally, love is not something another gives you. It is something—the most important part of yourself—which you give another, expecting nothing in return. Unselfish love is the most constructive force in one's life—the only antidote to the two most destructive forces, fear and anger. The love which the child is able to give is to a large extent conditioned by the love he has received. Although this is a long look ahead, the failure or success of his marriage may depend upon the concepts he has formed as to love, and his children's lives may be marred or enriched by the love he received as a child. Love your child, and let him know that you do; be laughingly demonstrative. But let yours be mature love, without possessiveness, without jealousy, demanding no return. Make yours a strengthening love, not a weakening one; a love that hopes for and supports the development of the best in the child, not a pampering, pandering, silly sentimentality. The expression of love should be a giving of spirit, not merely material feeding and care. Many mothers attempt to express love through a meticulous preparation of good meals and an undue regard for cleanliness, through giving their child "the best" instead of giving themselves—their heart and spirit. There is no virtue in keeping your child clean, well-fed and "looking well" if his spirit is starved. Rather an empty stomach than an empty heart; the stomach can be filled later, but the heart—probably never.

There are certain typical psychological emergencies that are likely to arise with children. Here are a few of those which parents and others may have to meet:

Attacks of fear. Fear may be either specific, aroused by some particular object or circumstance, or non-specific, an unexplainable outbreak of fear which is often seen in overanxious children. The parents' attitude toward fear is all-important; the parent who cannot handle his own fears cannot help children to handle theirs. Fear is natural, nothing to be ashamed of. Fear lies to you, possesses no power except that which you give it, no matter how much it threatens. The person who understands this will never have a panic, since he realizes that fear is in itself of little significance but is merely a temporary discomfort. The parent who believes this will indicate it by his actions and attitudes. In handling this emergency with a child it becomes a matter of quickly giving temporary reassurance and, as this is attained, helping the child to look on the entire episode as humorous or interesting rather than with a feeling of dread. In childhood fear can be pleasantly conditioned so that people will enjoy it as an adventure. "Sure I am afraid, but how I love it!"

Outbursts of anger. Children are to a large extent helpless, living in an adult world they do not understand, controlled by forces of which they are ignorant. Frustration is a daily experience in their lives, and since the purpose of anger is to furnish the energy to overcome frustration, they are given to outbreaks of rage and temper. An aggressive child is potentially a most valuable citizen, but much depends upon how he is taught to use aggression. The adult's attitude should be one of respect for the fighter as long as he fights nobly, but of obvious boredom toward any other expression of anger.

If a child is angry, investigate the reason why; the anger may be entirely justified. Correct the situation causing the anger and pay no further attention to it. If there is apparently no reasonable cause for anger, the child is using it as an attention-getting device, or merely as a rather pleasurable expression of energy. Under such circumstances, ignore the child; go away and leave him alone that he may learn that such conduct is in no way rewarding. Anger is not to be treated as an ethical issue, but merely as a stupid waste of valuable energy.

Jealousy. This reaction in children is due largely to
fear of deprivation and is shown as jealousy of the relationship between parents, between a parent and a sibling, or
between an adult and another child. Jealousy is most
likely to occur in a child who has not been given a full
measure of understanding, mature, demonstrative love;
the only treatment is to give the jealous child so much
love that he has no fear of losing it. Many children,
especially when they are young, perhaps displaced by a
new baby, need reassurance in words—"I love you"—as well
as close, demonstrative physical affection. Let the child
know that you love him and believe in him. Do not laugh
at a jealous child; to do so is to insult him, and you will
never be forgiven. Remember, it is in childhood that the
seeds of pathological jealousy are planted.

Revolt against discipline. When this occurs it usually
means that parental authority is, or has been, used unintelligently. It frequently indicates that the parent is
both too easy and too hard, first blows hot and then cold;
he gives a child too much money, and then berates him for
not being thrifty and takes away his allowance. Discipline
connotes not punishment, but teaching, training, education and guidance, with a goal of self-control and self-
direction. It must be consistently persistent, understanding, intelligent and free of emotional bias on the part of
the adult. Disciplining a child is like training a growing
vine to encircle a pole which will protect it, support it
and later hold up the fruit it bears. The gardener does
not get angry with the vine if it wanders at times, but

patiently rewinds it and perhaps fixes it temporarily to the pole which it seems best for it to climb.

Reaction against school. Usually a child's dislike of school is due to one or more of a number of causes which may lie within the parents' control. Often the child has been brought up alone, not associating with other children, not understanding them or knowing how to play with those of his own age. Adults are polite to children with whom their children play, and allow the child to have every advantage. His peers, however, are just as eager to win as he, and rightly give no quarter. It is particularly important that from early years an only child be taught to share, to take turns and to realize that he will not always be "first" in every game, but that he sometimes follows, sometimes leads. When he understands this, he has just as much fun in one role as in the other—and he has many more invitations to play!

The parents' attitude toward school is contagious. If they looked upon school as an ordeal, instead of as a happy period when they were assured of constant companionship and interesting, challenging experiences, they must make a conscious, intelligent effort to prevent their child's catching this unfortunate dislike of school from them. School is the child's first great adventure, and he should enter upon it with eagerness, courage and the certainty that he will find many new friends—including the teacher! If in the home he has found parental authority harsh, unyielding, punitive, and to be evaded whenever possible, he will expect the teacher to represent the same type of authority. If, however, authority has been to him a helpful, guiding force that has kept his small world in order and enabled him to function happily and efficiently at his age level, he will expect the same thing of the teacher. Some children have trouble in school from the day they start until they are graduated from college or—what is more likely to be the case—until they leave school to go to work. Then they have trouble with their superiors! Be careful that the authority represented by you does not set the child against all authority.

If a child has acquired this unfortunate attitude, it should be corrected understandingly, but as speedily as possible. A little common sense, patience and cooperation between parent and teacher will overcome a reaction against school that may be compounded of a rebellion against authority, fear of a new situation, homesickness and dislike of stricter regimentation than that to which he has been accustomed. One thing is sure: the child must not be permitted to develop an escape reaction by staying away from school; he must instead be supported and helped to master what to him is an ordeal. He is going to have to go to school for many years; he is going to have to get an education; there is no escape, but he should be helped in every way to find school a happy experience from which he will derive pleasure in learning, intellectual growth and the wider social life which no home can supply. Children learn from teachers and classmates the valuable lessons of adaptation to life as it is experienced outside the protected environment of home.

Lying. To a child there is at first no difference between truth and lies. When a thought occurs, that concept is a fact as far as the child is concerned. Next he learns that there are two kinds of thought: one which adults go by and call "truth," and the concept which they call "lies" and say must not be used. Nevertheless, lies seem just as effective in getting one's way as truth—indeed, they are often more effective! It is natural for children to lie, and they all do. Do not take it too seriously; merely let them know that there are two media of mental exchange in the world—"truth" and "lies." They may look alike, but lies are counterfeit and people soon stop doing business with mental counterfeiters.

Stealing. Society is very much afraid of a thief and, largely to protect itself, punishes stealing severely. Spiritually, it is one of the minor crimes, and readily understandable in children. Children do three kinds of stealing: that due to the desire for adventure, that occasioned by deprivation (this being rare), and stealing that is a compulsive, sadistic reaction to emotional discomfort and unhappiness.

A child who is deeply disturbed emotionally may steal things he does not even want. He will give or throw away the things he has stolen, though they may be articles of considerable value. He may be seeking an antidote for his own discomfort through getting even or upsetting others, and through the temporary thrill of adventure. Find out what is making the child unhappy and correct that situation.

Rewards and punishment. The growth of a child's

nature cannot successfully be forced. Children must be given time to put down their roots, develop, and unfold. Approval from adults they love and discriminating rewards help them to do this. We all seek rewards, tangible or intangible. See that children are stimulated to greater intelligence and renewed effort by judicious rewards in appreciation of effort and growth toward maturity. It goes without saying that when a thing has once been given to a child, be it approval or a long-desired toy, it is his, and is never to be taken away from him by virtue of parental authority. If he misuses even his own possessions, they may be put away temporarily, with the explanation that they will be returned when he has learned to use and not abuse them. Wise parents must at times show a child that certain conduct has not met with approval, but they do not make disapproval retroactive. Punishments there must be, but let them be infrequent, dramatic and for the sole purpose of creating a constructive memory of a harmful situation to be avoided. Suitable rewards stimulate intelligence and effort; punishments retard both, causing self-pity and rebelliousness.

VII

First Aid for the Adolescent

ADOLESCENTS need psychological support, guidance and emergency assistance more than anyone else, and with them, psychological first aid pays high and continuous dividends in terms of happiness and usefulness. Adolescence occupies the period of approximately the second twelve years of one's life. It is a time of marked physical, intellectual, emotional and experiential growth. It is often distinguished by great idealism, and many religious conversions occur then. At the other extreme, in many adolescents there is a marked spiritual deterioration, perhaps because the individual is so preoccupied with material things as to leave no place for the spiritual aspects of life.

Fortunately, the church is giving increasing thought to the special problems of adolescents, recognizing their needs and the opportunity for religion to play a more vital part in the life of young people at a time when it can be of most constructive value. Those who associate with adolescents can by precept and example encourage interest in attendance at religious services. Like the school, the church has the same objective as the parents—

the good of the child; both these social institutions share with the parents responsibility for helping the child to develop his highest capabilities. Parents may be sure that their own attitude toward religion will be reflected in their children's lives.

Adolescents are part child and part adult; no one knows how much of each, and the percentage varies from day to day. It is hard to know at what age level they should be treated, and it is just as difficult for them to know how they should act at any given moment. They are supposed to carry responsibility and develop independence, as well as form new emotional ties, yet parents often treat them as if they were ten years old. In many instances adolescents may justifiably compare their situation with that of prisoners on parole—their actions are always subject to review; they are damned if they do and damned if they don't.

Adolescence is a period of confusion in aims, values and direction. Intellectually the adolescent has a thoroughly adequate machine but is without sufficient knowledge and experience to operate it competently. Emotional turbulence and storms are the most marked characteristics of adolescents; they ooze emotions. The volatile emanations are readily seen in girls, as they take little pains to conceal them and enjoy exaggerating every emotion they feel. Boys show the existence of strong emotions by trying to hold a tighter grip on themselves, in keeping with their exaggerated ideas of how a man must act. In both boys and girls there is increased physical and mental restlessness; they are mobilized to do something, just anything to expend energy, so they tend to over-act, to be extreme.

The chief needs of the adolescent girl or boy are these:

Adequate preparation in childhood to meet this period. Before reaching teen age, children should have been taught a certain amount of independence, cooperation, reasonable respect for authority and ability to get along with their contemporaries, with enough of the techniques of adaptation to enable them to keep at least their toes, if not their feet, on solid ground when the flood of adolescence threatens to engulf them.

Association with only the best type of adults and other adolescents. Since adolescents are highly suggestible, they are largely at the mercy of their environment. Their most important criterion is what others do. Their associates, therefore, should be likable, wholesome, stimulating and in every way first-class people—beginning with parents. Many adults, of course, are adolescent in their interests— perhaps because they did not acquire better values when they were young. Such parents set a poor example for their children.

A home of which they can be proud and to the atmosphere of which they contribute. Needless to say, this does not mean an expensive house. It means a home where the atmosphere is harmonious and stimulating.

Opportunity to expend energy in games, sports and physical work, all leading to increased coordination. They should learn to take care of their physical needs, to cook, sew, keep house, handle money, garden and do repair jobs around the home. Although girls need these skills more than boys do, it is equally important that boys know how to take care of themselves and their belongings, and learn elementary sewing, cooking and housecleaning. Boy Scouts are proud of the merit badges earned for home-making qualifications, and soldiers, sailors and marines whose manliness is unquestionable have found it not only necessary but diverting to be able to take care of themselves. Men and women both need to be able to get along without being waited on. A sense of personal independence is essential, and unless one can look after one's simple everyday needs, there is always a sense of inadequacy which weakens the ego.

Adolescents worship heroes. The boys may too easily worship professional baseball players or outstanding college athletes. The girls worship movie stars, and a large industry spends millions on advertising to take advantage of this tendency. An adult who remains such a "fan" is to that extent adolescent. The worship of professional athletes and movie stars is harmful largely because it diverts the interest from worthwhile pursuits. A natural, and what should be a useful, psychological void is being filled with dross and will continue to be filled thus unless something constructive is found to supplant it. One real friend a few years older who is a fairly good athlete, one attractive young woman whose example one would be glad to have one's daughter follow, will have more real value than dozens of glamorized idols.

Adolescents should be encouraged to engage in physical

activities, particularly those sports and hobbies which will be pleasant and useful throughout life. Baseball, football and basketball are good absorbents of energy, but most adults cannot continue participation in these "rah rah" games except as spectators.

Useful sports and hobbies—pursuits in which they may be participants and not spectators—are now available to all young people. Tennis, swimming, skiing, mountain climbing, sailing, skating, fishing, camping, horseback riding and even flying can be had by practically all adolescents who are encouraged to go after them. Coordination in the use of the body stimulates coordination of intellect and tends to decrease both physical and emotional tension.

Ability to employ intelligence is particularly stimulated by skill in using one's hands. It is well to learn fine sewing, cooking, painting, sculpture, amateur carpentry and electrical repairing—in other words, to develop manual skills in combination with intellectual and aesthetic interests. Adolescence is the time for this.

Most antisocial conduct comes to light in adolescence. It may be due to poor preparation in childhood, to parental neglect or inconsistency (too easy one moment, too stern the next), or to unfortunate associates. Most antisocial behavior may, however, be attributed to lack of an appealing, socially acceptable opportunity to express physical energy.

Adults whom the children can respect and like—who do not repress them, who do encourage and help them in their coltish activities, who understand their emotional sorties, and who above all never tease or laugh at them—these adolescents call blessed. Even these adults, however, had best not demand obedience, for they will get none except that which they have earned by developing their qualities of leadership. Open doors for the adolescent, more and more doors; quietly plug up, unknown to him, ugly drains through which his energy might seep away.

The emotional storms of adolescence (though not all children have them) may be storms of joy or of fear, anger, jealousy, frustration, hurt pride, remorse and the feeling of unworthiness. Treat these as unimportant thunder-showers, intense, short-lived, acutely devastating tempo-rarily, and all signs of the storm will quietly disappear, even from memory. Practice being a receptacle where the emotional drippings of adolescence can safely be deposited —emotional drippings bound to collect as young people are being "tried out" in the process of being fitted for life. Under such circumstances wise parents do not give advice, do not moralize, *do not tell about their own lives*—they just listen and try to act as if they understood. One should never give advice during these emotional storms because that is the surest way of being misunderstood and the quickest method of losing one's rating as a support to adolescents. When the emotional storms have passed, *never* refer to them again. Above all things do not say, "You are too big to act this way; you should know better. You should treat me with more respect!" That line is futile; they act that way because they are big—and they do know better. And our conduct has probably not won any right to their respect. Most adults have not distinguished themselves by their actions, and they may be sure that adolescents are the first to know their faults. They are usually just too kind and ashamed to mention them!

Sensitiveness is, next to intelligence, man's greatest inherent psychological asset; it enables him to perceive and to understand his environment. Sensitiveness is, however, both an asset and a liability. It is an asset if employed externally; a liability if directed inwardly. The adolescent is the most acutely sensitive being on earth; he has just arrived at a full development of sensitiveness and is sensitive at all points. You cannot approach him from any direction without touching a new and, even to him, unexpected tender spot. These are the ways in which he may express his sensitiveness:

Perfectionism—being above reproach.
Deception—trying to hide faults.
Aggression—attempting to frighten away critics.
Inadequacy—admitting failure before it occurs.

Of course all these methods that the sensitive person employs to escape criticism are equally inefficient, and one lesson adolescents must learn is that there is no way to escape criticism. Mother, father, sisters, brothers, wives or husbands, friends and associates will criticize them all their lives, no matter what they do or do not do. During adolescence they must learn to extrovert their sensitiveness and become oblivious to flattery and criticism, both of

which are thoroughly undependable and grossly misleading.

The adolescent is unduly self-conscious; he is aware of
his inadequacies and afraid that other people will notice
them. He is supersensitive to what he believes others
think of him. He must learn that they seldom take the
trouble to think of him; they are too busy with their own
fears and troubles, and if they do think of him they are
probably not thinking what the adolescent is afraid they
are thinking.

Adolescence is the time when children should learn the
value of *charm* and how to practice it. Charm is the
lubricant of human relationships and should be used
regularly and freely throughout life. It consists of a sincere
spirit, a sense of humor, a ready smile, a "yes, thank you,"
or "I am delighted," a courteous answer, an effort to enter
into every situation and do more than one's part, and a
refusal to be shy, or at least to act shy. Above all, charm
involves consideration for others, enthusiasm, optimism
and eagerness to see and experience all that is good in
life. Charm pays big dividends!

Remember that the adolescent is extremely suggestible.
Use this to his advantage whenever you truthfully can.
Tell him that he was charming, wise, logical, strong, brave,
amusing or showed good judgment in a situation. This
will encourage him to redoubled efforts in the future.

The *imagination* is tremendously active in children and
adolescents; since they are only partly aware of the realities
of the world in which they live, their mental energy

naturally turns to imagination. The adolescent's imagination has the additional drive of newly activated instincts; what the individual cannot attain in reality he can partly enjoy through imagination. In adolescence children begin to employ imagination constructively, to use it as a sounding device, a radar to push through the fog of ignorance and inexperience in search for some valuable realities. Imagination should now be directed more and more toward constructive planning. Some people, particularly those who are unsuccessful in life, retire within their imagination and try to find solace there; a poor, unsubstantial solace it is.

Probably the one greatest conflict that adolescents have lies in their *dependence-independence* situation. While developing independence, they are still physically, financially and to a large degree emotionally dependent. There is much misunderstanding about independence. No one is truly independent but merely relatively so. All people must answer to some authority, be it another individual or society, a wise chief or God. The best-adjusted people are those who understand this and live accordingly. Children need to escape the emotional domination of parents, to follow other leaders and friends. When the child is about fourteen years of age, parents should drop their authoritative role and become mentors, aiding the adolescent to find independence and others whom he can trust for further guidance. The job of the adolescent's parent is patiently to pick up the pieces and say, "It is not so bad; you will fix it better than ever." Never say, "I told you so."

The sex instinct comes to sudden and full strength in adolescence. Sex manifests itself from earliest childhood, but many parents are too obtuse or ignorant to be aware of it. The children are very much aware of sex. Not knowing what it is all about, they believe it is a fairyland soon to be entered; then, with sudden intensity, it is revealed— a tremendous drive with few and inadequate directing forces. Even the adults seem puzzled about sex, judging by their acts. Until adults regard sex as a responsibility, and the closest, most sacred communication of spirit (instead of merely a matter of pleasure), sexual immorality will increase among the young. They merely imitate and magnify what they find in their adult prototypes.

Boys are entirely aware of the existence of the sex drive. They accept it for what it is, then make their choice as to what they will do about it. Girls are not always aware of all, or at least the early, manifestations of sex. With them sex starts with a desire for attention, dressing and acting to attract boys, and petting. All this leads from one step of physical contact to the next, so that when finally their choice of sex response is required, they are already rather deeply involved. Adolescents need to be unostentatiously chaperoned, kept in hand, kept on a time schedule and kept away from alcohol. Parents and adult friends must use intelligence to accomplish this, never admitting to the adolescent that they are doing it, but remembering that it is during the last third of the date that the young people may lose their heads. It is just as important to protect your son as it is your daughter. Intelligence, planning, kind and loving comprehension, an attitude of believing in your children, are all most helpful—but do not believe in other people's children too much; be neutral about that.

And what shall you tell the adolescent about sex? Practically nothing will be necessary—adolescents who are "told" about sex usually know more than they are told! When the child was very young, parents should have discussed sex as a natural part of life, answering each question as it was asked, at an age level suitable to the child's understanding at that time. In the home the discussion of matters relating to sex can be as normal a part of conversation as the weather and the daily events of home and school life.

The adolescent does, however, have certain specific, urgent and important problems pertaining to sex with which he needs assistance. Once again, it is no time for moralizing or talking about what *you* did; give him the facts and try to cement these facts to him with appealing emotions.

The sexual act, in itself, is not sinful. But sex relations before marriage are unwise and under adverse conditions can be most painful and disillusioning. Grapes are sour and bitter before they ripen, good when they are ripe; so is sex.

Boys and girls need to develop self-discipline. Without self-discipline they must remain slaves to their instincts all their lives. Demanding abstinence from sexual relations until a person is ready to assume full responsibility for the act is society's way of helping people acquire this self-control.

A girl who is promiscuous has less chance of getting a husband. If a boy gets what he wants without marriage why, he may ask, should he assume that responsibility? Also, the girl has a much poorer chance of keeping a husband after she gets him.

Pregnancy is a very real danger in spite of all the contraceptive devices. Any practicing physician will tell you this. Nearly every doctor sees many pregnant unmarried girls, usually deserted by the boys, who come to him seeking an abortion center—of which there are many, operated by gangsters who employ incompetent medical assistants and buy police protection. Not only does the girl run enormous physical risks, but there is no guarantee against blackmail.

Most girls tell physicians that these pre-marital experiences gave them no pleasure, or as they express it, "I got nothing out of it"—except a baby or an abortion, possible sterility, and a degrading experience destructive to self-respect. These girls have suffered for nothing and have memories that haunt them for life.

Some girls trick boys into having intercourse, lie to them about being pregnant, and threaten to tell their parents, all to get the boy to marry them. And many succeed!

The adolescent needs to know these facts about sex relations. In addition, he must be made to realize that the manner in which he handles his sex life is his choice; he will pay the piper or collect the reward, depending on that choice. Of one thing the adolescent may be sure: one never "gets away" with anything; no one does or ever has —in the long run.

Sentimental affairs are, however, to be expected among adolescents, and girls and boys may gain valuable knowledge by having a number of sweethearts in their own social group. In this way a girl comes to know what boys are really like, and the same is true of boys in regard to girls. Parents can do much to further wholesome relationships by their attitudes, the welcome they give when young people visit the home, and their lack of criticism or interference. Instead of thinking it a nuisance to have boys and girls "always around," wise parents encourage adolescents to bring their friends home. The boy's parents in particular should be grateful that he feels free to bring his girl friends to his home, and that the girls like to come. The girl's mother likewise should be happy to know that her young daughter is in your home.

"Twosing" is to be discouraged while boys and girls are still too young for marriage. There is not only safety but knowledge and interest in numbers. Every boy and girl during adolescence should have a string of sweethearts. Childhood romances terminating in marriage are sweet to the romantic onlooker but usually bitter to the participants. To be a good mate one must understand and like the opposite sex, and to remain faithful after marriage it helps to know that people are very much alike, that if you are not successful in one marriage you probably will not be in the next. People have to learn what love is, and it may do more good than harm to have one's heart broken before marrying!

Early marriages are to be avoided. They usually occur between unstable, immature personalities or as an epidemic in times of war when not sufficiently discouraged by parents who are themselves half-crazed by war. Only too often early marriages are a girl's escape from an unpleasant home. Girls and boys should not marry until they are physically, psychologically and financially fit for that experience. They should be able to support themselves both materially and spiritually. All this is for their own good. Parents frequently think it is generous, kind and understanding of them to allow sweet young love to mature in a marriage which they encourage and finance. This is comparable to allowing a student flyer to take a six-motor plane up and land it alone, in a fog, before he has ever soloed in a training plane. Marriages are becoming one of the most unsuccessful of our American social institutions, largely because young people are not adequately prepared in adolescence for their most exacting life work.

VIII

A Review of Principles

WE have now covered most of the usual emotional problems likely to confront you—or your family and friends. If you have read and studied the preceding chapters, you should be able to handle these problems more intelligently; you should now have some of the tools needed for building a happier, more successful emotional life. Before taking up the techniques of meeting specific psychological emergencies, let's review the principles we have learned.

In this review, it may help to imagine the course of life as a steeplechase. The time is now, all are entrants, and everyone must run. Those who have beforehand acquired some knowledge of the course are prepared for the usual hurdles and have a better chance of taking them successfully. The more usual obstacles after infancy are starting school, making and keeping friends, adjusting to the ideas of others, competition, adolescence, adjusting to sex and learning to conform to the mores of society. On every course are the obstacles of youthful confusion as to purpose, work and psychological divorce from emotional dependence on parents. Adults, usually woefully unprepared, blithely tackle marriage, children, sickness, frustration, financial reverses, success, failure, loss of a loved one, middle age, retirement and, finally, old age. If people live long enough they will have to take most of these jumps. In the process, at one obstacle or another, many come a cropper. When this occurs those who are hardy, wise and spirited will remount and take to the course again, realizing that the race is not over until the finish line is crossed. But one can be saved many a hard and costly fall if one knows better how to ride and is more familiar with the expected course of life.

People do not understand that what occurs in the course of their lives is but a repetition of the experiences of all human beings. While all hope to get an education, go to work, marry, have children, attain a degree of success and more or less live happily ever after, most people have little knowledge of how these objectives are to be accomplished, and few have any conception of what happens after the age of thirty-five. When the unexpected does occur, there is bewilderment, confusion and the feeling, "This could not happen to me!"

The sense of bewilderment is nearly always present when one is suddenly and acutely hurt, either physically or mentally. People do not expect misfortune and pain to be a normal part of life in spite of the axioms "Into each life some rain must fall"; "Man is born to trouble"; and "The way of the transgressor is hard." An adult has attained psychological maturity only when he has arrived at an intellectual and emotional acceptance of the fact that he must inevitably meet difficulty, pain and frustration at intervals throughout life. When he makes this knowledge a part of his philosophy he is immunized against the cruel thrusts of fate, can deal with them more comfortably and will live efficiently. Adaptation is relative, but he who has some understanding of what is to be expected in an ordinary lifetime, who has acquired the philosophy of acceptance, and has learned the technique of adjustment adapts better than others.

Living successfully is largely a problem of personal engineering, requiring knowledge and skill in the use of the principles and techniques which govern human adaptation. The techniques are of particular importance, since there are many wrong ways of meeting a given situation, and only a few correct approaches. If one does not know the correct techniques, and employs the trial-and-error method, he is almost sure to go wrong. The need to study the successful techniques of others, adopt them, and profit by experience is apparent.

It is important to remember that everything which is part of man is normal. This includes his actions, his thoughts, his feelings, his aspirations and his relationships to others. With this acceptance of man as he is, you will never be astonished, shocked or revolted but will realize kinship with every other human being. Some persons have a tendency to look for what they consider morbid and to find an unwholesome satisfaction in discussing it. For you there must be no love of morbidity, inasmuch as you do not believe that there is such a thing. Ignorance of man's true nature is all that stimulates and supports an interest in so-called morbidity, since, in the psychological as in the physical world, everything that occurs in nature is natural.

Try to free yourself from all prejudice—racial, cultural, religious and geographic. While prejudice is harmful to those against whom it is directed, it is even more injurious to the person who harbors it, inasmuch as prejudice causes him to carry an unnecessary, painful and handicapping burden.

Understand the importance of trying to find release from grief, anger, guilt and frustration by talking to some wise adult friend about your feeling and thus act out your disturbing emotion.

Having found release by "talking out" your troubles, make yourself take up constructive activities, so that you may get further release through actions which will give you a sense of accomplishment. This is frequently carried further by finding new interests and objectives. In so doing, do not put yourself under too much pressure, but use your own inner tensions as a stimulus to accomplishment.

Some experiences temporarily shatter an individual's concepts of life and leave him lost and without direction. This is the time to rebuild these needed, useful, protective ideas of life—and to rely upon the faith which you have found sustaining.

When under emotional stress, be sure to take reasonable care of your physical health; eat, rest, exercise and sleep, so that your emotional distress will not be further complicated and prolonged by even temporary physical deterioration or illness. People who are in trouble have a tendency to neglect their physical condition, at times even to punish themselves or others by physical neglect. Under such circumstances one must find ways to bring physical relief and comfort.

Remember to play the bases in life, not to steal them, not to expect short cuts, not to cut corners. Only the best in thought and conduct is good enough for a human being. Never under any circumstances let yourself when under stress do anything that will hurt your self-respect. You, like everyone else, sooner or later will have to work through deep troubles, but you're safe if your foundation of self-respect is intact.

No matter how badly you feel yourself, remember that kindness, patience and understanding of others are the best balms to heal your own wounded spirit. These virtues you must nurture in yourself until they become second nature. Let it be a rule of your life that you will under all circumstances try to be kind. No matter how much you suffer nor how much you are provoked to anger, be kind. To whatever extent you can do this, you may consider your life a success, for the kind person is loyal, courageous and forgiving. Kindness and love are the only antidotes for anger. Repressed anger is one of the greatest sources of mental anguish; the truly kind person does not suffer from repressed anger or vent it on others. His kindness allays anger and helps the angry person to function objectively and intelligently.

Patience pays big dividends. Patience is the ability to

wait until events run their course, knowing that if you do, your opportunity will come; luck will turn your way. Success is largely a matter of being able to await the opportunity patiently, and then seizing it avidly. Patience is especially needed in all human relationships. There is a constant, if unrecognized, battle, in the psyche of most of us, a battle between the ego demand "I must be first! I will be important. You listen to me!" and a deep sense of inadequacy acquired in childhood which says, "You are not much. You cannot do it. They will find you out." Even when we possess a healthy, strong ego we barely win the battle of keeping self-doubts outside the citadel of the soul. We do this by bringing up a large army of "I's" and a series of rationalizations. Most of us are impatient of the other person's "I's" and protective rationalizations, and would rather parade our army of "I's"; therefore we are likely to be self-important with others. If you are trying to help other people you must learn to keep "I" out of your conversation and bide your time and opportunity patiently. A patient man is armed against adversity.

Understanding is an ideal; it can be approached but never reached in its completeness. It is the one thing human beings want and need from each other. While you are sincerely attempting to understand, you are justified in appearing to understand, so that you may not interrupt the valuable if tenuous contact with another. In time, your understanding will become that which you now simulate.

Human beings help one another, have meaning to one another, share their lives on the basis of an inter-action or reaction which takes place between two personalities. This reaction is hard to describe or explain. Based upon understanding, friendship and affection, it is something new which two personalities produce when they come together, and this third factor in turn does something to and for both of them. This reaction can appear either as an abrasive or as a lubricant. When you are trying to help other people, you must learn how to remove or ignore abrasive personality traits and to employ the lubricants of kindness, patience and understanding, so that healthy and constructive bonds may grow between you and those you are helping.

. Part Two .

TECHNIQUES FOR MEETING SPECIFIC
PSYCHOLOGICAL EMERGENCIES

IX

Techniques for Meeting Specific Psychological Emergencies

THERE is bound to come a time in your life when you, like everyone else, come up against emergencies in your family, or that of a friend, which you must help to handle to the very best of your ability. What you have learned so far in these pages about meeting personal emotional problems should help you help others through periods of acute distress.

In dealing with people in trouble it is well to remember that time and nature have a tendency to heal many situations and much suffering. While you do not often say this to those who are suffering, you know it is true. Your attitude, therefore, can be one of sincere optimism: "You will feel better soon. This will soon pass, you will find that matters are better than they seem now." Emotionally ill people, however, may hold to and chronically accentuate their troubles. If as time passes people show no tendency to recover from their distress, this may indicate that their suffering is not the result of a recent or immediate occurrence, but is instead evidence of a deep-seated illness of personality. Such illness is a job only for an expert and demands immediate, skilled, medical psychiatric attention.

The Technique of Imparting Bad News. It falls to the lot of most of us, at one time and another, to be the bearers of bad news, it may be to a stranger or friend, or to a loved one. One can learn how to perform this painful task in a way that is wise, kindly and technically correct, so that the recipient is hurt as little as possible, is supported during the period of suffering, and is perhaps prevented from sustaining an enduring psychological shock. Death, crippling or hopeless disease, grave injury, accident, disillusionment, acute danger, unexpected insecurity, sudden financial reverses, loss and complete frustration of long-held and important expectations are serious examples of this situation. While the sad news must necessarily be revealed to those who are affected, and who must adjust to a radically changed situation, it should be remembered that there are often many painful petty facts which are better left untransmitted, such as malicious gossip and things which may cause unnecessary, weakening, personal disillusionment.

A person never knows when he will be called upon to meet such an emergency. It may occur as unexpectedly to the informer as to the person who is to be informed, but everyone—regardless of ability to meet such situations—sooner or later is faced with the necessity of doing so. It is therefore well to prepare your mind for this eventuality by accepting the fact that on some occasion this will be your difficult duty. Do this now by imagining yourself in such a situation, and know the technique of meeting it so that you will fail neither yourself nor others when the obligation must be discharged. To do this well, you must forget yourself, be objective, discount your own feelings, remembering only the job to be done and how it can best be accomplished.

When you have to impart bad news it helps, or course, if you know beforehand something about the personality and character of the person whom you must inform. Perhaps you already know that he is sensitive, apprehensive or aggressive; hysterical or phlegmatic. Perhaps you know that he has learned to take pain in his stride, that he is only unusually susceptible at the moment because of some other recent misfortune. Regardless of these facts, he must be informed, but such facts will make a difference in your approach. The perceptive and sensitive person will comprehend more easily and fully; the apprehensive person must be protected from his undue fears; the aggressive individual, from sudden and perhaps unwise actions. The hysterical person must be safeguarded against fatiguing emotional outbreaks, and the phlegmatic individual encouraged to talk. One who has already suffered much may not only be keeled over by this new blow, but he may unnecessarily fear another. If so, he must be led to hope that this is the end of his misfortune and that from now on fate will be kind. On rare occasions there are people so sick that they must be spared further bad news until they are stronger, but this is indeed rare and you should not use it as an excuse to escape a painful duty. The decision to delay telling bad news should be reached only after thoughtful consultation with physician, wise relatives or counselors. In general, people should be told of their misfortune promptly, as soon as the protective setting can be arranged. For you to indicate your belief that they are adequate to meet a situation and to accept pain helps them to do so. Your friendship, trust and belief in them is indictated by the fact that you brought the information as promptly as you reasonably could.

Whenever possible, bad news should be imparted by a friend who is a loved and trusted person—better still if the informer has a spiritually strengthening personality. If there is any way to prevent it, bad news should never be told by a stranger. Unfortunately, there are a few people sadistically inclined who either wish to hurt people or morbidly desire to witness their suffering. Others are careless, and a few are selfish. The inexperienced newspaper reporter who telephones the home to ask as yet uninformed parents the details of their child's death in an automobile accident has little consideration for the feelings of others but is concerned only with his scoop. Those who seek morbid excitement would do well to remember how such an occurrence would affect them. Consider how you would want it done if you were the person being told, then think how the other person will take it if it is done in that way. Being himself, however, he might not react as you would, and so you may need to think of another way in which to tell him.

Before breaking bad news, surround the individual with

all available protective and comforting influences, such as his own environment, friends and favorite relatives. Build a sustaining emotional atmosphere around him before telling him. Once again, this means friends, friendliness and understanding. Do not be abrupt, but lead up to the subject rapidly and avoid suspense. Refuse to be subtle; instead, be kind, direct and sincere. The telling of bad news must be done quickly, skillfully, gently and thoroughly—not allowed to dribble out. At times some bad news must not be told; then do not let it be wheedled out of you.

Plan what form of help you will employ when the reaction occurs, and remember that the reaction is usually delayed, so that you must wait for it. Most people think of how they will break bad news, but they seldom plan what they will do afterward. Devise a way to help the person while he is digesting what he has learned. Keep him busy, continuing to talk, thus more or less cushioning the sudden "sinking in" process. By so doing you will drain off surplus emotion and help him retain a normal poise. Later he will be grateful to you for keeping him from going to pieces. There is, of course, a natural expression of grief which should not be inhibited, but undue emotionalism may get beyond control.

A similar psychological emergency arises when you yourself are the recipient of bad news. You wish to meet it gracefully, adequately and efficiently, and you would like to make it as easy as possible for those who are kind enough to perform this unpleasant task. Prepare yourself now, in your mind, for the fact that perhaps someday, most unexpectedly, you will have to receive serious bad news. Decide that you will accept inevitable misfortune, that you are able to stand anything and that nothing will ever be too much for you to assimilate and deal with. Realize that you will never be asked to adjust to more than you can tolerate and that your attitude will be, "Thy will be done. I know that God is with me, directing and supporting me at all times and under all circumstances." And when you suffer, do not be too proud to let others know this, nor yet so filled with self-pity as to prolong suffering unnecessarily.

Accidents, Injuries and Sudden Acute Illness. Among the specific psychological emergencies which people are called upon to meet, to handle objectively and efficiently, perhaps the most frequent are accidents, injuries and sudden acute illness. Even though the family may be well-adjusted individuals, these emergencies create a psychological crisis because they are unexpected, and necessitate making important decisions and plans when the people concerned may be too stunned to think. Under those circumstances you, as a close friend, may be asked to help take the responsibility of making important decisions for others. Whenever possible, get professional advice and consult the family so that you may be supported in what you do. Try to cover all possibilities, and push through whatever action is indicated, ready to accept blame if any accrue to you. When the emergency subsides, pass the responsibility back to where it belongs, and try to make each one feel that it was his good judgment which prevailed. Remember, strength is built of adversity and misfortune, they develop fiber and power. Help another, but do not weaken him. Point out always, "You did it—you can meet anything!"

In case of accident, severe injury or sudden illness— *think!* Turn off your own emotions as you would a dripping faucet. Turn yourself into a thinking machine. What is wise, how to do it, what not to do—these are your concern. Help the family to think; keep constantly before them the necessity for thinking wisely and acting efficiently. Only when everything has been attended to can one afford an emotional outburst without great injury to others.

Listen carefully and be able to repeat accurately what the physician says, first, that his advice may be followed; second, that the family who are not present may be told the exact facts, unembellished and with nothing missing. Remember that the family have the right to know the facts, all the facts, and that they must never be deceived.

If the condition is likely to be fatal, the physician should break the news, with the friend standing by. In these situations, see it through; remain available until the crisis has passed. It is not merely a matter of helping for a moment, even though the responsibility was entirely unsought, when a crisis like an automobile accident is thrust upon you. God has given you a job, and you are to do it thoroughly. You have for some reason been elected to a grave responsibility and given the opportunity of serving unselfishly and without thought of reward or even thanks— the greatest opportunity man ever has, and all too rare.

Do not spoil the job by saying in the midst of it, "I have to go home and get my husband's dinner," or "My wife will be worried if I am not home on time." Instead, take the attitude, "He can go hungry this once!" or "I will explain when I get home."

In these emergencies you may sometimes be requested to make practical arrangements, even to work out immediate financial plans. In such instances, secure the information and present it in a few concise words, thus driving facts home, rather than assisting in the collection of irrelevant arguments and unimportant details. You will always help, comfort, support and strengthen those who have trouble and confusion thrust upon them. You will never say, "What can I do?" See what is to be done, and do it. In every instance sustain all reasonable hopes that the others may entertain. If the condition is critical, say so— after you have surrounded the family with every possible support. Let the family accustom themselves to the idea that the situation is grave, perhaps hopeless, and thus be better prepared to face it—but only if the outcome is inevitable.

In case of an emergency call on others for assistance without hesitation, even though they are unknown bystanders. *Take leadership*. The people of this world are crying out for leadership. Develop every bit of it you have. True leadership, next to unselfish love, is a human being's and society's greatest asset.

The world greatly needs indication of direction, coupled with support and patience—in other words, leadership. But few people are willing to assume the responsibility, frustration and criticism inherent in the job of management. The people of the world cry out for leadership; loving, strong, firm, understanding direction. Nearly everyone can develop some of this quality, provided he learns to think functionally, objectively, comprehensively and in over-all terms.

To be a leader for a moment, be it in a big or a small way, is giving and demonstrating the best in one's self. It is a promise for the future of mankind.

Crippling Illness. Sometimes an individual learns that he must adjust his life to a handicapping physical illness, and families find that they too must adjust to such a situation. The illness is seldom the calamity that it first appears, but improper handling may give rise to unnecessary invalidism and unwise attitudes on the part of members of the family. If you are called upon to help, take the attitude that a certain amount of misfortune is the lot of all human beings and that there are compensations in every situation; that the misfortune is better accepted, not dwelt upon or bemoaned, and that the compensations should be actively sought. Help deal with the difficulty realistically, by securing all possible technical assistance to correct and minimize the handicap, and urge the use of this aid. Suggest that the handicapped person receive psychological reeducation for the better use of his mental assets and physical reeducation for the most efficient utilization of his remaining physical abilities. Both the mind and the body have unusual reserves provided for emergencies, which the average person does not employ until such needs arise. Mental and physical science have progressed to the point where people need not go through life discouragingly handicapped. A friend or relative's most helpful attitude is that the disability is a handicap only to the degree that the patient allows it to be so. Utilize the patient's interests and assets to the nth degree. Help him to know and use not only the resources of his family and friends, but those of the community as well. If he cannot go out to find and follow new interests, help to bring in to him whatever is feasible. Do not hesitate to call upon other members of the community for assistance. Friends, church and social groups respond generously and helpfully to requests for home visits to shut-ins. They supply diversified interests, keeping patients in contact with the community, and adding new friends.

When a person is crippled by illness or accident the family are at first sustained by hope; after the greatest possible improvement has been reached and months or years pass with no further change or improvement, they may become weary. It is at this point that you, as a beloved relative or friend, realizing that the family are physically and emotionally tired, can be invaluable. You can bring in new reserves of optimism, provide transportation, act as a "sitter" to make it possible for the family to get out for recreation. You can read aloud, encourage handcrafts, arrange to spend definite regular times with the invalid as a help to both the patient and the family. Sometimes a family falls into the bad habit of staying too close to their job, thus losing their social contacts and not knowing how to go about getting back into the world. Here you may be of assistance by occasionally taking them out of the home and doing things with them. It is amazing how many people under such circumstances have no one with whom to go to church, lunch, the theater, or even for a walk, particularly when they have been giving all their time to a semi-invalid. Here's your chance to help these relatives or friends, who are themselves practically "shut-ins," to renew social contacts.

Mental Illness. All human beings need a better understanding of mental illness. Mental illness is not different from any other sickness, but the family in which it occurs may not realize this and therefore be frightened about it. Such illness is curable. With proper and immediate treatment the patient has every chance of getting well, and treatment by a psychiatrist in a modern sanitarium or a good mental hospital is frequently a pleasant experience and nearly always a rewarding one.

People who are mentally ill should receive prompt, expert and sufficient treatment. The earlier the treatment the better the chance for good results. A qualified psychiatrist should be secured, with a reputation for knowledge, skill, experience, persistence, good judgment and excellent results. (In this connection, see pages 183-187.) Many patients are not cured because they discontinue treatment too soon.

In dealing with a person who is mentally ill do not deceive him—ever—for any reason! Mentally ill persons often feel very much alone. Treat them as if they were normal. As a relative or a friend you should listen to them, withhold your opinions, make no suggestions as to cause or treatment other than, perhaps, "Let's get the doctor; he is an excellent physician; you do as he says." The build-up which friends give a physician is important in all types of sickness, but especially so in mental illness. The patient is confused, frightened, ignorant as to his illness and filled with direful imaginings. Choose a good doctor, and then praise him to the sky!

Be gentle, understanding, patient and without curiosity. Treat everything that happens as a natural occurrence. Tell the truth, but do not parade it; never argue, or disagree, or disapprove. Yet you need not lie. If asked whether you hear voices and you do not, say you do not. If asked your opinion about a distorted or implausible psychiatric interpretation, say that you do not know, but that anyone may be mistaken in perception or interpretation.

Remember always that the emotionally sick and mentally ill person is deeply disturbed. You see only the island rising above the sea of consciousness—this island is merely the peak of an underlying and obscured mountain of deep-seated illness. The various symptoms evidenced by the sick person indicate that assistance is needed and are often clarion calls for help. Do not hesitate to give it. Forget the old idea that mental patients are dangerous; they commit far fewer crimes than do those who are not mentally ill. You need not be in the least afraid; you must act with assurance, using a pleasant, light touch. Your lack of fear will lessen the patient's fear as nothing else can.

As for the family, first dispel their ignorance and prejudice. Make them see that immediate treatment for the patient is essential, that no quack, no cultist, no semi-equipped physician should be permitted to enter the picture. There should be no waiting to see if the patient will get better; no hoping he will grow out of it; no sea voyage or hunting trip, no cross-country tour; no listening to old wives' tales. Medical science knows how to treat and cure mental illness; everything except psychological medicine has failed. The family need reassurance; be optimisic. Help them to treat the patient as a normal member of the family; not to dwell on unusual behavior; to ignore eccentricties; to attach no importance to unusual remarks and actions, or the patient's false ideas and perceptions. Let them understand that the patient is still their loved one; he is not really changed but merely appears temporarily different. Just as with measles or mumps a person appears different—so much so that it would be quite frightening if it were not so well understood—so a person who is mentally ill is only temporarily different. The family cannot expect to understand what it is all about, but to the doctor the entire illness is logical and comprehensible. The family should not try to understand the underlying pathology, because just as an organic pathologist must be trained for years in his profession, so must the physician be educated in psychopathology. Leave that to the doctor; it belongs in his field. Do not start talking about Oedipus complexes, masochism, identification and other psychological jargon. Above all, do not talk about your "nervous breakdown" or your Aunt Susie's mental illness!

If a mentally ill patient is to be admitted to a hospital, or if property rights have to be temporarily cared for, minor legal procedures may have to be attended to. Usually these procedures are simplicity itself. The purpose is to protect the patient and to secure treatment. Unfortunately, legal terms such as "commitment" are used. Commitments should be considered as no more serious than registering a patient in a general hospital; usually it is just as easily terminated. Remember, the hospitals want to cure patients, to get them out of the hospital and back into the community; and good hospitals are curing most cases of mental illness. So do not hesitate to use the legal procedures provided for this purpose, as they are in all instances confidential and such an everyday occurrence that there is no news value attached to them.

Alcoholism. There are few adults who are not sometimes called upon for sympathy, counsel or definite action in regard to an alcoholic, who may be a member of a friend's family or perhaps of their own. If such a friend or relative uses alcohol unwisely, he and the family need help. In such a case the following principles should be adhered to:

1. Recognize that the person *is an alcoholic;* face this squarely and bravely.

2. Realize that this condition is an illness. Alcoholism is the symptom of a serious emotional maladjustment that must be corrected as a part of curing the individual of the alcoholism.

3. With the physician as counselor, the family should determine that this condition must be cured and that they will do all within their power to bring this to pass.

4. Do not find fault with a person who is drinking; the family should refrain from upbraiding him.

5. Do not warn the alcoholic to "be careful," to try to drink reasonably. The time for that is past.

6. Do not tell him that he must not drink. Usually he already knows that.

7. Do not ask him if he has had a drink. If he is an alcoholic, he will have to be cured before he stops. If he is taking alcohol, he will lie. He will hate you for making him lie and despise himself for having lied. What does it matter whether he took a drink at this particular time? You know he is drinking; he will have to be cured before he stops.

8. Do not in any way attempt to deprive an alcoholic of liquor. If this must be done, call in a physician at once and let him do it.

9. *When the person is not drinking* and is mentally alert enough to understand, his problem should be calmly discussed with him. Insist that he undergo treatment, primarily for his sake, but secondly, for

the sake of his job and his family. Do not warn or threaten; employ reasons which will appeal to him.

10. He should be placed in the hands of a physician who has had success in treating alcoholism. Do not temporize with unscientific methods of treatment, such as "building-up exercises" and drug cures. Every time a person is unsuccessfully treated for alcoholism, it reduces the chance for his ultimate recovery.

11. Do not try to keep an alcoholic's family or friends from knowing that he drinks. This is a fact that is neither to be hidden nor driven into the open. Do not let him deceive himself or protect him against the knowledge that others are aware of his drinking. In the long run this is not a protection, and the force of public opinion brought on by himself—not by family or friends—may induce him to seek treatment.

12. *The person must face the fact that he is an alcoholic;* that he is suffering from an illness that is beyond his control, and that no alcoholic can successfully treat himself.

When a person is actually drunk, the best thing to do, if this is possible, is to stay away from him. It will, however, be necessary for someone to keep his eye on him, to know what he is doing, and to be on the watch to see that he does not hurt himself. Always remember that when he has been drinking an alcoholic is an illogical, primitive, unpredictable person. Keep sufficiently out of his reach so that he cannot reach you either physically or by what he says. Do not be disturbed if his actions and general demeanor are ugly and unbecoming. Neither agree nor disagree with a person who is drinking. Instead, be noncommital, never critical, but friendly, kind, gentle and reassuring. It is necessary to treat a person who is under the influence of alcohol as you would a patient who is passing through a delirium or suffering from some other form of mental illness. If you can do so, get him to bed; keep him away from people. If these measures fail, the best thing to do is to get him into a hospital where professional assistants can take care of the acute situation.

When an alcoholic has recovered from a drinking episode, he is usually unduly optimistic about the future. He is likely to say that his trouble is behind him; he knows he can handle this himself. In spite of many failures to do so, he will continue to make such assertions. He cannot handle his alcoholism himself. Therefore try to get him to seek advice; urge him to be honest with his adviser. If he will not seek assistance at this time, see if you cannot prepare the way for future help by saying you believe that he will need it; ask him whether, if he should ever need help in the future, he will be willing to seek it then. Usually an alcoholic will agree, though that does not necessarily mean that he will remain in that state of mind after he has gone through another drinking episode.

Do not laugh at or laugh with an alcoholic. Simply remain noncommittal and friendly. Do not aid and abet alcoholics in finding fault with others, because they practically always find fault with anyone who knows that they drink, particularly the spouse, employer or even a friend who has helped them. It is not wise to correct them, even after they are no longer under the influence of alcohol. Although he is not then drinking, following a "spree" an alcoholic is not able for some time to use his intelligence or emotions constructively. There is an actual temporary impairment of mental powers and distortion of point of view as a result of the alcohol (which is a potent drug), and these symptoms require something like six weeks before they disappear. That is one reason why he should be in the hands of a physician, and if possible in a neutral environment, while he is being actively treated.

Do not let an alcoholic bully you; do not be frightened by his threats. Remain calm, gentle, patient and kind. If he threatens suicide or injury to others, do not hesitate to call for outside assistance, preferably medical, but lacking that, from friends or the agencies which society provides.

Attempted Suicide. Not only alcoholics but others who are emotionally disturbed may attempt suicide. A person who attempts suicide is temporarily mentally ill. It is never the act of an adjusted adult who has accepted hardships and frustrations. No normal person commits suicide, even though he seems normal in every other way. Suicide is abnormal and is due to illness—depression, hysteria, self-pity or deep anger, all of such severity as to constitute illness. Sick persons sometimes rationalize attempted suicide on the basis that they do it to protect someone else, but suicide harms others more than the continuance of a difficult situation. It sets a bad example for loved ones and undermines the morale of all who know of it. It is fundamentally a revengeful act against self, the world and God. That is why it is quite properly considered a great sin. The threat of self-destruction is openly or subtly employed by many small-spirited women to harass others, but some carry the bluff too far. Suicide is a selfish, self-centered expression of discontent. To entertain the idea of self-destruction is evidence of a mistaken and distorted personal psychology; actively to consider suicide is a sin. The thought of suicide, even the wish for death, probably enters the mind of everyone, but such an idea can be easily and permanently routed by the definite decision that this one will never do, under any circumstances or provocation. A person who approaches being well-adjusted has decided that he will never use escape reactions; and suicide is the "granddaddy" of all escapes. Having permanently closed that door, he is ready to face life courageously and successfully. The positive renunciation of suicide makes it impossible for anyone to commit such an act, even should he later become ill. Unfortunately, many people do not understand this and as the result of a physical, mental or social illness they become temporarily suicidal and must be protected, not only until they have recovered from the illness but also until they have acquired a healthy philosophy of life.

This condition, therefore, is to be treated as a form of illness. See that a suicidal person has immediate and complete protection. Do not leave him alone for any reason, no matter what he says. Take no chances! Remember that a person who has once attempted suicide is likely to try it again until he is cured—and he is not cured in a few hours or even days. If only they can be kept alive until cured of illness, most suicidal people will get well under proper medical treatment. Secure the most competent medical and psychiatric attention available. It is best to place a suicidal patient in a closed, well-conducted psychiatric hospital that has provision for handling such cases; that affords the patient every protection, gives him good psychiatric treatment and makes him understand that society will not and cannot lightly accept such anti-social conduct.

In the event of an attempted suicide, sometimes a close friend has to take the situation into his own hands to secure protection and treatment for the patient. Frequently the family are stunned, ignorant of the true significance of the act, or through false pride they may assume a covering-up or inconsequential attitude toward the occurrence. Do not hesitate to explain to the family in plain words that this was a suicidal attempt. This is no time to mince words, for the majority of suicides could be prevented if those who know the patient would handle the situation vigorously. Suicide is not a matter that a person should be allowed to threaten even jokingly, for you never know how serious he may really be.

People who threaten or mention suicide, perhaps with some malice, dramatics and a desire to distress others, if taken seriously, sometimes accuse others of having no sense of humor, or even of putting the idea into their heads—all of this being additional maliciousness. A sense of humor is out of place when a person threatens murder, either of himself or of another.

When they hear of someone who has committed suicide, very suggestible persons become afraid that they may do likewise. They say, "Wouldn't it be awful if I killed myself?" The correct answer should be, "Yes, it would be awful! Do you vaguely think that you want to do it?" When they reply, "No!" they may then be told that such a thought enters the minds of everyone; it has no significance, and since they do not want to commit suicide, they cannot.

If you should become involved in an attempted suicide, make every effort to save the person's life. Many apparently hopeless situations have been retrieved. Protect the person three times as long and as well as you believe necessary, and then try to see to it that he has continued treatment to cure him permanently of both his mental illness and his sick philosophy of life. Help the family understand the seriousness of the situation; do not let them gloss it over. Get them to realize that one unsuccessful attempt does not mean that the danger is over; that will not be *until the patient is cured.* Do not indulge in the false comfort of believing that people who talk about suicide never commit suicide. Realize that they are subtly or subconsciously appealing to you as a friend or relative for assistance, and when this appeal is ignored through lack of understanding on your part, the danger is increased. The individual may feel either that you do not care or that you do not know how to give him the help he needs.

Persons who have attempted self-destruction frequently feel guilty, and they should. The only mitigating excuse for them is that they were sick and not themselves. Yet they should understand that even sickness is not an excuse; for if they cultivate a right philosophy of life, even though ill, they would not attempt suicide. Under the circumstances they must do what everyone else frequently has to do; namely, acknowledge that they made a serious mistake and that from this experience they have learned a great deal.

If you are called upon for help, do your best to prevent an undue sense of guilt or self-recrimination on the part of members of the family. Do not admit that they are even partly responsible; reiterate that the patient was mentally sick, but that the family did not know how seriously ill he was.

Urge his family to treat the patient as if he had been ill or in an accident, to let him talk if he wants to, but not to ask him unnecessary questions or manifest curiosity. Leave questioning to the psychiatrist, who knows how to handle this illness under protecting and supporting conditions.

The family should keep the patient busy and as cheerful as possible but without false or forced gaiety on their part. Overcheerfulness jars just as does music that is foreign to one's mood. There can be a gradual but not too sudden return to normal feeling tone. Try to help the family avoid being exposed to the curiosity of tactless friends, and do not yourself try to explain matters to other friends or discuss the situation with them. The information is not yours to divulge, and since anything you say may be misinterpreted, say nothing.

The family should never, even later on, avoid the mentioning of a relative's attempted suicide, and they should certainly not attempt to conceal the facts from any physician who is caring for the patient, either then or later. Both the physician and the patient are entitled to have the physician know that the patient has attempted suicide; let the physician judge the importance of it, but in talking to him the attempt at suicide should not be minimized.

Death. Death is almost always sad, and sometimes sudden and unexpected, necessarily an occasion for the realization of loss and loneliness, and frequently a stimulus to thoughts of insecurity. Human beings are dependent upon near relatives and close friends; death brings the realization that they are more alone, have less to support them emotionally, and so gives rise to hitherto unrecognized insecurity and unacknowledged self-pity. People are unfavorably conditioned to death. In childhood they feared it and did not understand; indeed, they were frequently morbidly afraid. As they grew up, children were at times surrounded by adults who put on long faces, black clothes, and were sad in unison. Most of these trappings of death are barbaric, many of them being customs hanging over from ancient times and primitive people who lived long before the Christian era. Human beings love drama; birth,

marriage and death are dramatic, and have been drama-
tized from time immemorial.

The sadness felt in regard to death is in some degree due
to conditioned emotional reactions, duty, custom, self-
pity, insecurity and loneliness. It is sometimes purely a
selfish reaction. "I have lost something I want." The
more dependent a person is and the less adequate, the
greater this selfish reaction and the longer it persists.

As a close friend, when you are called upon to help those
who have had a death in the family, get them to talk; do
not discourage their crying, walking the floor, wringing
their hands—giving full natural expression to a normal
emotion. Do not advise them to be brave, to bear up for
the children, to put up a good front. On the contrary, if
the emotion is too self-contained, open them up as if you
were opening a carbuncle; that is, open it in all directions
and let it drain. If necessary, apply a mental poultice to
bring the emotion to a head so that it will burst. Under
these circumstances, do not be afraid of emotion or even
of hysteria. When the bereaved person is emotionally ex-
hausted you can then suggest that he will sleep and tomorrow be stronger. No one is more difficult than the "brave
person who, with true Anglo-Saxon pride, just will not
break down." Repressed grief causes further grief, as well
as depression, inefficiency and illness. It is to be hoped
that in time human beings will learn not to be ashamed of
their natural, healthy, emotional expressions.

The loss of a beloved individual, or a person upon
whom one is emotionally dependent, is a shock no matter

how well one may be prepared for it. The bereaved person should be surrounded by those he loves and his closest friends. He should not be left alone, even though he asks for seclusion until he has recovered from the shock of his loss. It is understandable that everyone should want to do things for him, and yet it is best that he be encouraged to attend to everything himself, even the funeral arrangements of the one who died. He should be kept busy and given very little time to think; he can do that after he has recovered his normal poise. The kindest thing his friends can do is to think of every little detail he should attend to and encourage him to do this. It is a good thing for him to have to think of other people at this time, for in trying to help and comfort them he will find truths which will comfort himself. He should eat, sleep, see people and carry on with his usual duties. With encouragement he may even take pride in how normally, courageously and wisely he is dealing with the situation and helping those around him, and at the same time not be ashamed to let others witness and share in his emotional reactions.

Death affects people differently, depending upon their philosophy, religion, emotional stability and the circumstances under which the death has occurred. Sometimes death temporarily destroys the desire to be happy. Some persons feel that it would be wrong for them ever to find happiness again. Since happiness is an important factor in both health and constructive living, this attitude must be altered as soon as possible. So it is wise to point out that the loved one would have wanted those who are bereaved to find happiness again, and that the greatest tribute he can pay to the person who was truly loved will be to live a useful, happy life, carrying on the things which the loved one believed in and stood for; this is the surest way of seeing that his spirit does not perish from the earth. It often helps to review the happy events in the life of the person who has died, pointing out that no stone was left unturned to bring about a recovery from his last illness and to make him comfortable. Later it may be wise to point out that a long period of mourning is a mistake. This increases self-pity, undermines health, makes life harder for family and associates, is unchristian. Mourning is a subconscious desire to recapture in a distorted form some of the emotion felt during the life of the other person, but since death is final as far as this earthly life is concerned, it is impossible to do this.

Older people regret unduly the death of a young person, bemoaning "a life cut off in its prime" and saying, "His death was so sad because he was so young; he had so much to live for." But, actually, there is no reason to be sorry for a young person who dies. Remember that he enjoyed life because he *was* young; for him life was ever new, without problems and responsibilities; he missed some interests and happiness, but also much suffering. It is often self-pity, loneliness and selfishness that cause old people to be needlessly sad over the death of a young person. To die in the full bloom and strength of one's youth is in many ways a blessing. The really sad situation is one in which young children are left without a mother or father. Death should be considered a normal, natural phenomenon; just as is birth, it is truly painless as far as the individual is concerned and nothing to be dreaded. "Death is but the groom who bears the lighted taper to the outward room." It has been said that no one is fit to live until he is willing to die. The doctors who are now so greatly prolonging old age may be doing neither the individual nor society a kindness. It might well be of more benefit to mankind to emphasize and concentrate on improving the *quality* of life rather than the *duration*.

Some people who have been getting a little weary under the pressures of life take the death of a loved one as a convenient quitting place, or an opportunity for a long, sad vacation; so they just wilt. They should not be allowed to continue in this disheartened state of mind. As soon as they are really over the shock, they should be helped to remember that there is one less warrior in the world and it is time to close up the ranks; there is more now for each of us to do. Following a death in the family, or any other severe or long-continued emotional crisis, when all details are cared for and the person is back in his stride, a change of scene, associates and thoughts may be wise—but this should be thought of as a natural, normal expedient, not as a permanent withdrawal from life. This should not come immediately but soon after the death. The mind holds some mental pictures entirely too long, as can be shown by how low in spirits one may be for several days after a bad dream. Sad memories and grief are not constructive, so a change of scene is helpful in order that new, realistic, happy pictures may replace the gloom which nearly always follows a funeral.

Death may radically change one's way of living, necessitating major social readjustments on the part of those who are left behind. If possible, these changes should be deferred. At any rate, they should not be discussed until the person has recovered from the reaction to death—be this grief, fear or loneliness. When the individual has recovered, he should either be presented with the problem and helped to solve it or, if he is not adequate to meet the situation, the family or those closest to him should hold a conference and decide what plan is best and how this will be presented to him. The fact is that after a bereavement many people waste years of their lives and all of their money drifting. They are lost souls, a burden to themselves and to others. Women who lose their husbands are often happier if they go to work—or, shall we say, continue to work, but in a new field, since we will suppose that prior to their loss they did work as homemakers. The truth is that many people are lazy; others have good intentions but are dilatory. A person who has a plan of life and follows it is an adjusted, happy person, so after a death each person in the family should have work to do and do it. It is particularly valuable if they can render useful service to another. Work, more than anything else, decreases emotional tension, loneliness and self-pity.

Through working for those things which the person who has died found worthwhile in life, it is within our power to continue the spirit of the one who is gone. It helps to understand that when people die their spirit truly remains with those who care for them. People have frequently kept alive the spirit of one whom they loved and respected to such an extent that those who died long ago are, like Christ, more alive than most of us on earth today. The spirit of a fine person never dies, and if our love be great enough we can keep this spirit alive and useful.

When people are in trouble, especially when a loved one has died, you, as a friend, should try to find out what they believe in and help them to use their faith constructively. Assemble and employ all the spiritual forces in which the person believes. These may be religion, good sportsmanship, courage, loyalty; call on and utilize them! Some people are afraid to speak to another of such sentiments, but do not hesitate to do so, for spiritual factors are the most potent tools for helping toward readjustment. Just as man cannot live by bread alone, so intelligence will not always sustain him; in the final analysis, his only strength is in the things of the spirit. Although he may not know how to use it, every individual has a reservoir of spiritual strength. We can help him to draw upon this inner resource in his time of need.

ALIVE *

Because you live, though out of sight and reach,
I will, so help me God, live bravely too.
Taking the road with laughter and gay speech,
Alert, intent to give life all its due.

* From *The Spires of Oxford and Other Poems*, by Winifred M. Letts, published by E. P. Dutton & Co., Inc., New York.

I will delight my soul with many things,
The humours of the street and books and plays,
Great rocks and waves winnowed by seagull's wings,
Star jeweled winter nights, gold harvest days.

I will for your sake praise what I have missed,
The sweet content of long united lives,
The sunrise, joy of lovers who have kissed,
Children with flower faces, happy wives.
And last I will praise Death, who gives anew
Brave life adventurous and love—and you.

Fortunately, not all emergencies are so dramatic or tragic for the individuals concerned as those discussed, but certain emotional situations are fraught with dangers not only to the individual but to home and family life. Many of these emergencies are brought about through inefficient handling of those emotions which are common to all, such as anger and fear.

Acute Manifestations of Anger. The purpose of anger is to mobilize the individual to fight so that he may win, yet anger stifles intelligence. If he wants to win, he must wait until anger subsides, then act intelligently. If you are called upon to help, the emergency treatment of anger is kindness, gentleness and waiting—then forget the outburst and, above all, help the angry person to forgive himself.

Tantrums are hysterical evidence of retained childish reactions to frustration, and should be treated as such by family or friends. Do not be upset or frightened by temper tantrums. The best way to treat a person who is having a tantrum is to leave him alone, as in some instances these outbreaks are fanned by an audience. If the tantrum is directed toward you, ride the storm through and do not consider that you started it. Tantrums are a dangerous habit that began in childhood. A person who indulges in temper tantrums is like a loaded gun; a tiny and unsuspected pull on the trigger may cause a mighty explosion. If a person makes a habit of exaggerated anger, urge him to seek psychological treatment.

When you are with a person who is angry, remember that emotions are contagious, and guard against catching his anger. "A soft answer turneth away wrath" still holds true. You can take it—and take pride in being able to do so. If you are trying to help others you must upon occasion be able to take unearned punishment.

Try to understand the reason for another person's anger. Frustration, the touching of old sore points, prejudice, fear and an unwillingness to bear pain are frequently the reasons for anger. Once you understand the real cause for the outburst you are in a better position to help.

Try not to take anger too seriously; then it need not be intolerantly repressed or primitively expressed. Anger should be understood as a primitive instinct, to be borne with, laughed at, and talked about. The intolerant repression of anger results in emotional volcanoes, depressions and physical sickness, while a tolerant choice to bear with one's primitive nature, to modify it, and express it for the good of humanity is an entirely different story.

A person who frequently explodes with anger is sick.

Get him to a doctor. Neither argue, agree or disagree, laugh at, nor try to reason with an angry person. Appear not to be shocked. Keep out of reach, lend a friendly presence, and try to save the pieces of his self-respect.

When *you* are angry, remember—

1. You are wrong—absolutely wrong. You want to act in a primitive, destructive manner.
2. Perhaps unknowingly, now or previously, you invited being sinned against. Notice how people who get angry frequently are the tactless ones who ask for or court trouble for the excitement of meeting it, usually badly.
3. Be quiet. Be kind, sweet, gentle. Be a door mat *when you are angry.* Nine times out of ten you will find it was all a misunderstanding. The surest way of "getting even" with a person who treats you badly is to give a chance for his own shame and guilt to occur to him rather than fight with him and so crystallize his sense of righteous indignation.
4. You are angry. Don't say it—don't do it—it is not worth it.
5. If necessary, three days later tell the other person what a fool you were to be angry with him (rather than cogitate on how mean and nasty you would like to be).

Unpleasant Arguments. Frequently a person finds himself, though a bystander, part of an ugly and dangerous argument. Tempers are lost, friends are parted, enmity is crystallized, misunderstanding becomes a way of life—indeed, sides are taken on a senseless and unnecessary controversy.

Some few people have become specialists in putting out these fires. Seldom recognized as such, they are the beloved members of their group. Such a person knows that arguments are always in error. The argument is won by the person who can exhaust his opponent by talking longest. Usually neither opponent presents truly cogent and applicable facts. In general, it is purely an emotional and completely unintelligent procedure. Whichever side wins generally serves to temporarily establish an untruth or partial truth.

Thus you should have no respect for an argument. It is like a squall at sea which may capsize a small boat. You should never believe in winning an argument merely to establish your ego and hurt another's self-confidence. You do not want such an empty victory. So always let the other man have the victory, if necessary, but save him from that defeat if possible.

Arguments come out of anger and fear, both primitive instinctive reactions, always leading in the wrong direction if expressed primitively. If you alone are concerned, quietly walk away from every argument and forget it at once. If you become involved in a situation where this is not possible—think. You are going to try to put out this fire with humor—loving, understanding humor—and so you have only one try at it, so think and bide your time. While the argument proceeds, be genuinely and impartially friendly with both parties. Make no comments until you have thought of something kind, humorous and complimentary to say to both. If called on to express an opinion, *don't do it.* It will not help until tempers are quenched. Under such circumstances, an understanding grunt is a good substitute.

See how many grass fires of argument you can put out, it will take practice, but it is excellent training in the techniques of human relations.

Fear and Panic. The frightened person should always be treated as a sick person, one who suffers acutely. Immediately he should be insulated against stimuli which might further increase fear. Get him into a situation in which he feels safe temporarily. Act as if you feel no fear yourself. If the danger is real, say so, but show him his strong points of defense and help him to fortify these positions. Remind him that fear is the normal stimulus giving rise to courage, then help him to find his courage and bring it into play. Lead him to hope that this is the darkest moment, and that his situation will fortunately improve soon. Assure him that you will help him out of this present jam, although for the moment you may not know how you are going to do it. In even the strongest person, fear may coincide with moments of great weakness, and you can help him through such a crisis. Unobtrusively remain with a frightened person until the panic is over. Keep him from action which will later hurt his self-esteem. Reassure with actions as well as with words. Do not deny your own fear, but dwell on the hope and the things which give you courage—your confidence that all will be well. Each person when faced with disaster is given the strength to weather it, if he will but use that strength.

Your attitude should be that fear is a normal experience through which everyone goes; fear in itself is unpleasant but usually not significant, as it possesses little factual value. If one is afraid, it is best to meet the situation head on, calmly and steadily. Walk with a frightened person up to and through apparent danger; divert his attention in any way you can until the danger passes. Talk quietly, kindly and reassuringly, saying in effect, "Things are never as bad as they seem; there is always a way; we will find it together." Call on your courage, and share it with the other person until he regains his own. Help people to look on fear as one of the interesting adventures in life rather than as an unpleasant experience to be dreaded and avoided. Never forget that fear is the normal stimulus to courage, of which everyone possesses an inexhaustible supply.

When the attack of fear is over, try to remove its traumatic effect on memory. Do this by helping fearful persons to discuss, understand, discount and even enjoy fear. Help them to see that running from that which frightens them is frequently more dangerous than walking up to the supposed danger. In the presence of fear and danger, keep calm, think, and act quietly and with self-assurance. One such person has prevented many a panic!

One of the worst results of fear is that, having suffered it, visionary and imaginative people foresee trouble. It must be admitted that they get a morbid kick out of doing this. Daydreams are a normal childhood indulgence. The habit of looking for trouble and suffering it vicariously—encouraging *dread*—usually starts in childhood. People with the habit of dread must be cured of this malicious state of mind, and it usually requires a psychiatrist to do this.

Disillusionment. Most people have a tendency to live by established order. As they grow up they are trained to relate themselves to social patterns, customs and beliefs. Thus, to a certain extent they live by concepts which may later be found to be illusory and incorrect, or at least partially so. For example: a certain religion is the true religion, the one and only religion; men are brave; women are virtuous; children are sweet; marriage is beautiful; judges are honest; true friends are always loyal; and so on. Many of these illusions are protective and perhaps necessary. Just as most good soldiers believe that they are coming through all right, so most people go through the world with similar protective illusions which support and comfort them in many ways.

When the established order is interrupted, however, when society suddenly changes its social patterns, customs or beliefs, when a cherished illusion is found to be completely untrue, many persons are seriously disturbed— sometimes only temporarily, sometimes permanently. Sudden disillusionment is frequently a calamity of no small proportion, not only to the individual but to his social group and to society in general. Individuals become confused, doubt all they have believed in, and lose faith in themselves and in others. They may stop trying, become cynics, adopt mistaken goals. Disillusionment may even precipitate an acute attack of what was, until now, only a latent mental illness.

Since an illusion is a misleading image, a mistaken idea, a false impression, an adult who is mature emotionally as well as physically and intellectually does not want to keep illusions. The loss of illusions is not something to be regretted, but a sign of progress, of growing from adolescence into adulthood. When confronted by someone else's sudden loss of illusion, the understanding relative or friend should think back to the illusions which he himself gave up, recall how he replaced illusions and dealt with the factual situations. The acquisition of insight into your own true nature, the nature of other human beings, and the fundamental laws of the universe requires courage, character, patience, flexibility and a fundamental belief that man, society and the universe are basically good. A shattered illusion does not mean that all is wrong, but merely that you went on the rocks because you were navigating by an unreliable chart. More accurate charts are now available if you care to use them. The world of truth is much more interesting, challenging and worthwhile than the one which you imagined.

Debunking is often employed ostensibly to destroy illusions, but more actually to inflate the debunker's own ego. Subconsciously there is the thought, "Tear down others, then I will appear greater." To those who truly understand, this exposing of the human frailties of the hero makes the hero greater. If with all these human failings, temptations to which he succumbed in moments of weakness, he yet rose to heights in which he accomplished the deeds that have made him rank with the great, he is more of an inspiration to the rest of us mortals than when he was looked upon as a god and placed upon a pedestal. Our respect and admiration go out to those who have achieved much in spite of weaknesses and temptations, who have had much to overcome in order to reach a higher level.

Illusions are often of our own making. The idealized person has not changed; he is still the same as he always was. As we grow into maturity, however, we see him as he is and should not, therefore, vent our disappointment upon him, but accept him and change our attitude to one in keeping with reality.

Rostand's *Chanticleer* affords an excellent illustration of a fine attitude toward the destruction of illusions. Chanticleer was honest in his belief that his crowing caused the sun to rise. When the golden pheasant tricked him into sleeping past sunrise, then taunted him with the fact that the sun had risen while he slept and that he had nothing to do with its rising, he did not give up crowing at sunrise. Instead, he still rose with the sun and carried on with what he considered his duty, rousing the barnyard with his crowing and fulfilling his responsibility as a leader—acting as he thought he should in spite of the loss of his illusion.

When a person has suffered a great disillusionment, he needs the support of friendship and understanding. Later he needs guidance in finding more worthwhile concepts to replace those he has lost. You must first help him to accept the situation as it is and not to make the mistake of replacing one false belief with another. Help him to take pride in his ability to see and accept the truth, and guide him towards the direction where you believe he will find truths which will support, strengthen and comfort him. Do not throw more hard truths at him while he is in the midst of his suffering, for he may not yet be strong enough to stand them. Your attitude is, "Yes, you went on the rocks when you thought all was well. You were shocked by it, but the tide will rise, and you will float free. The damage is not irreparable, and now that you know what these shoals are, and what led you to them, you are a better and more trustworthy mariner. The same opportunities for happiness and usefulness lie before you now as always. Your disillusionment will reveal these real opportunities to you, only now you know that you must actually navigate your own ship. I will tell you all I know about this and will find others to help you. You realize that you can no longer afford to run before the wind, hoping for luck if you encounter a fog. Knowledge and understanding will hereafter enable you to proceed more accurately and more securely."

Loss of Confidence. Closely related to disillusionment, though not always traceable to specific events which may have been responsible, is a lack of confidence in themselves and others which may become a chronic state of mind in some individuals, endangering both mental and physical health and robbing life of much of its joy. Many, perhaps most, people feel fundamentally insecure, fearing at times that they may not be fully adequate. This sense of inferiority develops in childhood and is frequently increased by difficult adjustments at puberty. As a protection against this sense of inadequacy the individual builds up a protective ego, based on parental love and training, education and successful experience. Naturally, life experiences as well as inherent ability enter into the individual's attitude. If overambitious parents have forced the child to attempt tasks beyond his capacity and he has suffered repeated failures, if his relationships with others have been unsuccessful, it is not surprising that he begins to distrust himself, then to reason that others, too, must feel that he is inferior. The degree of the feeling of inferiority versus the strength of the ego which gives rise to confidence varies in different people, so that some persons lose confidence more quickly and more completely than others do. Confidence in ourselves is related to the trust we have in specific individuals and in other people in general. When those we have trusted fail, or when a large number of people act in an unworthy manner, it is a blow to our sense of confidence: first, because it seems to deprive us of supporting outside strength; second, if those whom we regarded as superior prove ineffectual or untrustworthy, we seem forced to doubt ourselves. We feel much as we did in childhood when we relied upon parents, then found that they were not as wise or as powerful as we believed they were. Most people overvalue their sense of confidence. When it is impaired they feel definitely handicapped, depressed, unnecessarily helpless and completely defeated. These people do not realize that frustration is a normal part of life, that confidence is a by-product of successful effort, is always relative, and is not, therefore, essential to the success of an enterprise—provided human beings are willing to continue to make intelligent efforts in spite of past failures and fear of future failures. The trying may seem harder, the undertaking lack some of the joy that should accompany successful achievement, but the result is not necessarily impaired—when one does what he thinks he should do regardless of how he feels and in spite of his lack of self-confidence. Sometimes it helps to regain confidence in ourselves to reflect that others have more confidence in us than we have in ourselves, else they would not have entrusted to us the task of which we are afraid.

In the course of a lifetime, sooner or later all of us suffer a severe blow to our sense of confidence. As children we fail in school (though perhaps it was the school that failed!), later a marriage falls to pieces, a business goes bankrupt, an undertaking is a failure, people seem to have no use for us, or life slaps us down too frequently, so that personal morale suffers a crippling blow. The strong and understanding person comprehends that this happens to everyone, that it is an expected part of life. He is, therefore, only temporarily hurt; he picks up the pieces of his ego and tries to put them back together a little more intelligently, realizing that his ego serves a useful purpose in protecting him against his sense of inferiority. He says, "I am even more adequate than I thought—I have gone through this; I can stand pain and failure, rise up and try again!" He learns to believe!

> "I have learned something well worth while
>   That victory could not bring
> To wipe the blood from my mouth and smile
>   Where no one can see the sting;
> I can walk, head up, while my heart is down
>   From the beating that brought its goad,
> And that means more than the champion's crown,
>   Who is taking the easier road.
>
> I have learned something worth far more
>   Than victory brings to me,
> Battered and beaten, bruised and sore,
>   I can still come back again,
> Crowded back in the hard, fast race,
>   I've found that I have the heart
> To look rank failure in the face
>   And train for another start.
>
> Winners who wear the victor's wreath,
>   Looking for softer ways,
> Watch for my blade as it leaves its sheath,
>   Sharpened on harder days,
> Trained upon pain and punishment
>   I've groped my way through the night
> But the flag still flies from my battle tent
>   And I've only begun to fight."
>
> > "Camp of the Fallen" by Imogen Clark

As a mature adult you are likely to have opportunities to befriend and help many people who have suffered severe blows to their confidence. Listen while they talk, comfort them, make them feel that you have confidence and strength and that you will lend them from your store until they have regained theirs. Let your friendship be the bridge over which they pass to find confidence in themselves and in others. Dispel self-pity, guilt and anger; help them to comprehend the psychological and philosophical aspects of self-confidence. Perhaps they have been trying too hard, driving tacks with sledge hammers, striving to attain too much too quickly. Perhaps they have set their sights too high and must wait until life closes in a bit, nearer the range of their abilities and experience. But even so, encourage them to use their "bow chaser" once in a while. It is a long-range, inexpert shot which once in a lifetime makes a bull's-eye—and it is fun to keep trying. Help them to see this, get them to relax, perhaps to rest from the effort for a short time, to laugh and play a bit and recover their sense of perspective. Do things with them, play with them, give them more attention; show them your approval in every small way you can, and let them know that you consider them worthwhile. Help them rebuild their egos, assure them that they are very adequate, help them to do things successfully, and praise them for each success. Go off on a trip with them, or get some other friend to do so, remembering that a change of scene and quiet in which to think often helps a person to find his stronger self.

The Feeling of Being Trapped. This occurs when a

person finds himself in an apparently impossible situation. The following suggestions will be helpful:

1. Advise the individual to sit tight; things are never as bad as they seem at first.
2. Remind him that there is a solution to every problem, and this is no exception. Wait, and he will find it.
3. Call upon him to use his intelligence, and to take pride in his ability to do so.
4. Tell him that he must turn defeat into victory. Assure him that you will try to help him to do this, then make good on your promise.
5. No trap, jail or situation can bind a soaring spirit. Every trap has a weakness—look for it.

Loss of Employment. Employment is an important part of man's life, as it not only provides a livelihood but gives tangible proof of his ability, establishes his place in the world of his equals, and gives purpose to his life. The fact that he has a certain amount of success in his work helps his self-respect, and makes him feel that others respect him.

There is a difference between the changes which a youth makes as he shifts about to find suitable work and the loss of a position that may occur to a mature middle-aged man with family responsibilities. The youth can take the loss of a job in his stride and not be hurt by a period of deprivation; the older person is likely to be disheartened, to lose self-esteem and become depressed. His family and friends should be urged to help him by showing their appreciation of him as a person—whether with or temporarily without a job. They should never show lack of confidence in his ability to find suitable work again. Sometimes it helps for other members of the family to go to work, but not if this makes the customary wage earner feel that he is unequal to supporting his family. If the plans are thought of as only temporary, he may be glad to have this evidence of cooperation.

Encourage a young person to think through the reasons why he lost his job, and whether there is something he can do, some adaptation he can make, to avoid losing the next one. There may have been no lack of effort on his part; perhaps the boss wanted to give the job to a son or to an influential friend's son. While it may seem unfair, the young job-seeker can accept this situation which often occurs and which need not hurt his self-respect. Help him to forget his old job and to go about getting a new one immediately. Teach him to use intelligence in job hunting, to utilize community resources such as guidance clinics, vocational training facilities and approved employment agencies.

Help the older man who has lost a job, through no fault of his own but through circumstances over which he has no control, to accept this fact without blaming himself or harboring resentment against fate or any other person. Do not say to him, "You should have done this or that," but rather, "Now you can do so and so." Help him to understand that there is a place in the world for everyone.

Assure him that earning a living is not too difficult for him, and that he is a competent employee with the will to work. Do all that you can to rebuild his sense of adequacy; point out his assets, and think of constructive suggestions as to how he may use these. Be practical, and if you can help him get another job, do so. If you have doubts as to how things will work out, never let a person who is already discouraged know this; your confidence in him will bring out unexpected abilities. You might remind him of these words from Ecclesiastes: "The race is not to the swift, nor the battle to the strong, neither yet bread to the wise, nor yet riches to men of understanding, nor yet favor to men of skill; but time and chance happeneth to them all."

Financial Reverses. A sudden loss of capital or a seriously diminished income frightens and depresses people. It makes them feel insecure, gives rise to a sense of failure, and causes them to worry about their families. This negative reaction may be pronounced enough to paralyze the inherent ability to recover and to carry on. A great financial reverse may appear to the victim to bring dishonor and (particularly if he carries a large amount of insurance) make him think of suicide as a possible solution. He does not realize that money can never make up for the loss of a loved one or compensate to those who are left behind for the fundamental injury to their morale that invariably results from suicide. Only a person with a one-sided philosophy of life takes financial reverses too seriously; money is the cheapest thing in life and continually gets cheaper.

You should acknowledge the loss of home, business, etc., as heavy blows, but not knockouts. Urge the family to accept misfortune and to get into action, not sit and brood. What is, is; their concern is not with the past, but with the next step they are to take. Help them to adjust to a new scale of living, and like it, until fortune can be retrieved; if it cannot be, to accept that fact. Perhaps the wage earner may be happier with fewer responsibilities and lighter work in later years. If he is young, however, urge him not to give up trying. Get the loser to realize that his attitude affects the family, and the family in turn to see that the way they take misfortune reacts on the member who holds himself responsible. While they have each other, all is not lost. Help them to take the attitude, "Let's go to work! We can always have the things which really matter!"

Unpleasant Publicity, Notoriety and Scandal. Sometimes unwise action on the part of one or more persons involves the family as well as the individual concerned in situations that are emotionally disturbing to the whole family. When this occurs the individual who has been responsible fears public condemnation and therefore dreads facing people. Counsel him in this way:

1. Go about as usual. See people and be seen by them. Act as if nothing had happened. Be unusually nice

to everyone. Do not be on the lookout for slights or unkindness.

2. Make no excuses and give no lengthy explanations.
3. If you are at fault, it is best to admit it.
4. News grows stale fast, and it is always displaced by new excitement. People have a tendency to discount unpleasant publicity, and they forget very quickly.
5. Remind him that while his stock may be low now, it has not always been below par. It is his business to raise its value, to make people believe in him again and like him. Almost any intelligent person can do this if he will try.

Point out that nothing from the outside can hurt the personal integrity of any member of the family. As a group they are to be encouraged to deal with the factual situation, disregarding "what people say." Remind the family that others are not nearly as critical and condemning as the family feel they are. Apparent curiosity is often awkwardly expressed sympathy.

Remember that the person who is at the center of the scandal may be in more need of help than the rest of the family. The more truth in the gossip, the more he needs understanding and help. In the course of a lifetime, everyone makes a fool of himself a few times. This is usually the result of ignorance, it may even follow an honest and conscientious effort, and it is often due to accepting poor advice when the individual is under emotional strain. Help him to accept it as a lesson learned and paid for—

a penalty for acting while emotionally upset instead of waiting until thinking, good advice and principles of integrity prevailed. Grant that the scandal did perhaps reveal a rotten spot in his personality which hitherto he had not suspected, but bring out the fact that he has an opportunity to correct a distorted point of view or an improper technique of adjustment.

The knowledge that you believe in the person in trouble and trust him renews his confidence in human nature and in himself. Remind him that God and men wish to forgive him if his desire to do better is sincere and effective, and that he should forgive himself.

Antisocial and Criminal Conduct. When there has been conflict with the law or conduct that is likely to result in that, both the wrongdoer and the persons he has injured are to be considered. A person who commits an antisocial or criminal act is frequently mentally ill. He should be treated gently but firmly, and never—because of anger or fear—roughly. Punishment is psychologically wrong, is actually the poorest of deterrents, and interferes with the future cooperation on the part of the wrongdoer which is necessary as a part of character correction. But crime frightens and angers society, and so it reacts as primitively and unintelligently as did the criminal. For the sake of society, the criminal may need to be placed in quarantine, either temporarily or permanently, but our attitude should be one of intelligent sympathy.

The family or group in which such an act occurs should be told that crime is a form of illness, and that an aggressive and punitive attitude on their part will probably only crystallize antisocial attitudes. When a man finds that reasonable compliance with the mores of his group brings adequate rewards he does all in his power to comply. We are all to some extent guilty of breaking the laws of both God and man, and should therefore act with more understanding when others are the offenders. Punishment is one of society's most stupid conceptions.

The occurrence of antisocial conduct is often harder on the family than death; they feel stigmatized, guilty too, for not having taught the offender better. This may be true, but this is not the time for blaming themselves or others; that is water over the dam; the situation must now be met and all possible assets saved. They must consider not what was, but what is to be, and try to bring that to pass.

Many people who are not guilty are arrested—the word really means to be stopped—perhaps only to be questioned or protected. When people have been arrested, show no repugnance toward them; listen to their story. They themselves are shocked and do not appear to best advantage. Make allowance for this; help them to recover from their shock, fear, and anger. Treat them as human beings who are in trouble. Help the accused and their families to face facts so that they may do what is best for all concerned. The best legal counsel possible should be secured, either a private attorney or a representative from the Legal Aid Society or one of the other service organizations. He should be told all the facts, with nothing concealed, and trusted to do all he can.

Discourage hate and anger on the part of all concerned. Let your attitude be that of Christ on the cross: "Forgive them, for they know not what they do." No one wants to be antisocial or criminal; crime is the result of ignorance, accident, flaws in the social structure and illness, particularly emotional or mental illness. Everyone who is in conflict with society needs psychiatric examination and treatment. In general, do not expect the psychiatrist to be on the culprit's "side," to make unfounded excuses, and to help him escape punishment. The psychiatrist's function is to help the individual get well and adjust constructively to a difficult situation. This is especially true of sex delinquency, which society especially fears, does not understand, and mistreats accordingly. Sex offenses may be due to mental illness or merely to lack of maturity and are not therefore "criminal" except in a legalistic sense.

The family and the accused should in most instances accept the decision of the court. Some of society's methods are antiquated and at times unfair, in some particular, to an individual offender. The court, however, must interpret the law as it is written; accept this, adjust to the situation as it is, then later on you may strive to correct such errors for the good of society.

Imprisonment should be taken as an opportunity to learn to think and act more wisely when one is again granted freedom and independence. Many prisons provide time to study and facilities to further one's education, to learn a trade, to attain a healthy philosophy of life. Even in prison a decent and constructive life is possible. If this is not true in a particular prison, the family may well devote their energy to bringing about better prison conditions, that negative and destructive attitudes may not be fostered in persons who are already at odds with society.

A true friend will never desert the accused or his family, and never allow the family to forsake the member who is in trouble and who needs them now as he never did before. Stand by with friendly support and constructive advice. Visit both the family and the prisoner frequently, and while he is incarcerated do everything you can to keep him in touch with the outside world. Bring him good news, tell him of interesting family and community happenings, and leave with him happy thoughts to consider when he is alone. Ask him to share his life with you, to tell you the things he thinks and sees. Reinterpret these constructively from your more normal point of view, for under the adverse conditions, his is probably warped and he cannot see the forest for the trees. Treat him as if he were temporarily in a hospital or hospice. Help him and all who are concerned to know that society quickly forgets one's faults, failures and crimes, notwithstanding popular but erroneous ideas to the contrary. *One does not have to live down a crime, but rather to live up to the best of which one is capable.* We are told that there is rejoicing in heaven when a sinner is saved; there is on earth also. Why? Because we all do wrong, and when we see someone able to rise above his weakness it strengthens our own morale. Likewise, people who are dynamic enough to be difficult in society make the best citizens when they use their energy and abilities constructively. I know a leading citizen who frequently says at a dinner party, "When I spent three months in a state penitentiary . . ." He is proud of what he has made of life since his release from prison.

Unwanted Pregnancies. Largely because of society's punitive, unintelligent attitude, premarital pregnancies sometimes so frighten those involved that they may resort to antisocial action that is stigmatized as criminal. Except in the case of unmarried mothers, an undesired pregnancy which at first was regarded as a calamity usually resolves itself into only a minor psychological emergency. If the mother is married, but for any one of a number of reasons the child is unwanted, someone in the family needs psychiatric treatment. There are many reasons why pregnancies are unwanted. A wife may so dislike her husband that she resents bearing his child. She may feel that she has, and may really have, too many children, too close together. She may think that she is too old, particularly if the pregnancy occurs near the menopause. Often at such a time there is a sense of shame in letting others know that she is pregnant. Sometimes husband and wife agree that they cannot support another child. Occasionally the husband unfairly blames his wife for the unanticipated pregnancy and arouses in her a feeling of unjustified guilt.

If you, as a beloved relative or friend, are called upon for advice, first try to understand why the coming child is unwanted, then be practical and kind. When the mother is married, remind her of the joy she found in other babies. If there was no child previously, stress the fact that she and her husband have now established their home and are in a better position financially to have a child, and that she will feel differently after the child is born.

If the mother is unmarried, the situation is serious, as the lives of the mother and the unborn child are in jeopardy. Urge her to secure immediately whatever psychiatric, social service and religious assistance the community provides. Young mothers-to-be feel all too keenly the unchristian attitude that is still taken toward illegitimate pregnancies, and in desperation often attempt suicide; this occurs most frequently when the father deserts her and his unborn child. A psychiatrist is experienced in ascertaining underlying attitudes, and under his direction the relative or friend may be useful in working out with the mother the best and most practical plans for herself and the coming child.

Never, whether the mother be married or unmarried, advise abortion! Never advise any mother to give up her child. You can discuss adoption as one of the plans the mother may consider, but *she makes the decision.* Help her to face the consequences of this disposition of a child, and, if she adopts the plan as best not only for herself but for the child, help her arrange for placement through the approved sources. It should be remembered that in any pregnancy moods are frequently variable, and decisions may be changed with moods. Stand by, even though it may be for many months; never weight decisions or hurry an unmarried mother into making them. If the decision first made is wrong, in the months of waiting she will probably realize this before any action has to be taken. Situations change, and as the unmarried mother finds that she has friends, and becomes more accustomed to the idea that she is to have a baby, she is less desperate, more capable of intelligent planning.

It is a well-known fact that most pregnant unmarried women have abortions. From the medical standpoint this is most unfortunate; women need babies. It is too bad that society so stigmatizes the unmarried mother. The social order has arranged good homes where unmarried girls may quietly have their babies, and many do.

Take no part in helping another to find an abortionist —counsel against it.

Broken Engagements. The shock of a broken engagement, if one is very much in love or feels that it may be a last chance for marriage, can be temporarily devastating and give rise to acute and sometimes lasting emotional disturbances. Under such circumstances, young people in particular need assistance, understanding and counsel. Broken engagements occur not only between adolescents but also between older persons who have retained adolescent attitudes, who deal only in superlatives, dropping from the heights of love to the depths of despair. Both adolescents and adults should be safeguarded against impulsive, dramatic, suicidal gestures, real or for effect. Attempted suicide becomes known to others and makes it more difficult to recover from shame.

Be the understanding friend who listens. Let the person who has recently suffered a broken engagement talk to his heart's content. Although you know that the pangs of love will soon be a thing of the past and that a young person will probably soon be in love with someone else, do not offer this consolation; youth cannot accept it while suffering is acute, cannot believe it and does not wish to do so.

Remember that boys may be hurt just as deeply as girls, but that instead of overflowing with emotion they may withdraw, perhaps become cynical. To you, the object of his love may appear to be a little fly-by-night peroxide blonde, but to him she is a dream girl, a golden-haired angel. Take him seriously and try to get him to see this was just one girl, not all womankind. Help boys as well as girls to get quickly "back into circulation" rather than to brood alone for any length of time. A little later on help them to understand that they have not really failed, that no one is to blame; that for some reason unknown to them or you this marriage did not fit into the scheme of things, or that the broken engagement indicates a serious incompatibility which is much better discovered now than after years of disillusionment and frustration. Get them to see that such an experience helps them to be better prepared for marriage, that marriage is really a difficult undertaking, demanding not only love, intelligence and technical knowledge, but a measure of true unselfishness as well. Many a person has been a better husband or wife after a broken engagement because ability to love has matured.

To an older person a broken engagement is naturally more serious, as it often means a complete change in life plans. To an independent mature person, there is little that anyone can offer as advice. Here, too, being a good listener is frequently the best service that can be rendered. It is wise to avoid questioning which may seem to be curiosity; after the first discussion let the subject drop until it is brought up by the other person. Listen, but do not prolong useless dwelling upon what might have been. Encourage activity and fresh interests, especially the making of new friends. Try to keep people who have been hurt from becoming cynical, angry or self-pitying. Encourage them to believe in men and women and to trust them, even though one person may have proved untrustworthy. Neither criticize the one who has hurt them nor encourage them to do so. Do not necessarily agree with their criticism of the other person; they did, and may still, love that person, and to find fault with one to whom they gave loyalty hurts their own morale.

Marital Crises. Human beings, driven by instincts and holding as they do various intellectual concepts, have not yet learned how to get along with one another. To live amicably and in peace with others is the greatest problem of both individuals and nations, and how to do this should be taught and practiced in home, school, church and community. Only when it is, can we expect peace among families and nations.

Like most teaching that is of value to the individual, adaptation with consideration for others, the freedom of the individual with due respect to the rights of others, begins in the home. Differences of feeling, thought and conduct are bound to occur in families, usually giving rise to anger. When such differences arise between husband and wife, they can avoid a marital crisis if each will use intelligence and ideals rather than emotion to resolve their difficulties and differences. It will help if both of them will try to adhere to these resolutions:

1. Husband and wife will refuse to get angry at the same time.
2. No matter how they feel, they will *act* courteously under all circumstances. They will always be gentle and kind.
3. They will agree to defer action until emotions have subsided and the counsel of wise friends has been considered.
4. A marital crisis will not be regarded as an emergency; for the time being the best thing to do is—nothing!
5. Each will give the other the benefit of the doubt.
6. They will refuse to let a state of civil war exist; when is does, neither can "win."
7. They will never forget that two intelligent people are bound to disagree profoundly about some things. To some degree they may both be right.

Marital counseling is a most difficult responsibility. Do not be astonished or hurt if those close to you neither seek your advice nor accept it if it has been unwisely volunteered. Perhaps you are too close for them to be able to discuss the matter with you. This is particularly true in families; you must learn not to take sides but to guide the individuals to reliable counselors who are experienced in dealing with marital difficulties. They will see explanations and methods of correction unknown to the average layman. Most marital crises would never have occurred except for lack of knowledge, training and experience in personal relationships. Many can be solved through psychiatric interpretation and treatment.

Marital disagreements should be considered a "private fight." A friend or relative called upon for advice should "see no evil, hear no evil, speak no evil" of either party, but help the couple to work out a solution for themselves. He can always safely bring out the value of patience, tolerance, understanding, kindness, forbearance and the necessity for compromise. He can remind those involved that marriage is, like any other mutual undertaking, a gradually evolving situation which at times may be difficult, and that the very difficulties may make for growth and the development of a more workable companionship. Get them to ask themselves, "Is this my best self talking?" We are all inherently selfish and must consciously work to be unselfish, particularly in our relations to our partner in marriage. We cannot possibly have the same viewpoints —we have had different life experiences and are different personalities. Couples can be helped to be adult in their discussions; to beware of descending to adolescent levels; to avoid vengefulness, aggressiveness, wiles and infantile emotionalism.

Thousands of years ago the Greeks said, "Harmony is not an ending of conflict, but is a tension of opposites in which neither side definitely wins, but both function indispensably." In other words, it is not necessary, possible or desirable to attain perfect agreement in all things, but both sides must function to the end that there be a workable issue resulting from the disagreement.

Do not listen too willingly to complaints against a husband or wife; much of it is not meant, and to encourage such conversation fosters a lack of loyalty on the part of the person who is complaining. Your attitude is: "Do not complain; accept trouble as an expected part of life and do something to better conditions."

"Falling out of love" may be part of adult adjustment after the honeymoon is over. The romantic aspect of courtship wears off, and newlyweds wonder if they are still in love. The answer is that one cannot go through such an experience without some valuable remnant of affection and memories of good times shared together. When a loyal person loves, he never ceases to do so, even though hurt, disillusioned and rebellious. Help people to save the remnants of what started off as a good marriage and they will discover that there are more than enough left to erect a good marital structure. Most couples weather these first storms of married life and are better and stronger thereafter. Mistaken sympathy may unwisely influence what is existing as a delicate balance—in the wrong direction—and alienate people forever. Do not weight the scales!

Sexual maladjustments, alcoholism, the rearing of children, the earning and spending of money, the kind of friends one has made, lack of expression of affection and trying to fence another person in are the major reasons for marital disagreements. By talking things over, and if necessary seeking professional advice, these problems can be solved. An underlying reason for disagreements is often found to be the lack of consideration and attention shown one another. Both men and women want and need consideration and evidence of affection; giving these freely will help prevent or smooth our major problems.

Help people to see that divorce is not a panacea; it may sometimes be necessary, but it is really doing things the hard way. Take no stand in the discussion of a pending divorce except to caution against hasty, ill-advised, ugly and ungenerous action. When dangerous, smoldering emotional fires exist, neither fan the flame nor rush for an extinguisher. If the fire is not already beyond control those concerned have and can use the extinguisher of understanding, tolerance and forgiveness. They alone must decide whether their marriage is to continue.

If the marriage is destroyed and divorce is inevitable, in process, or already obtained, stand by with your friendship. Help divorcees to find new interests, particularly work, and to live full, busy lives. Stress the importance of growth as an individual, which may have been neglected in a marriage that proved unsuccessful, thereby lowering self-esteem. If divorce must be, let it be a clean, dignified break, free of recriminations and self-justification. Take the attitude that both husband and wife were good people but that marriage just did not work out for them.

Stand by your divorced friends. Defend them, not in terms of taking sides, but in extolling their good points. When people are divorced their spirits may deteriorate; they may take to drink, fall into slovenly habits and otherwise neglect themselves. Help them with your supporting friendship and a willingness to share your life with them while they pass through the difficult period of readjustment. Try to keep both men and women from remarrying hastily on the rebound, or from marrying an extramarital partner whom they no longer love but feel they must marry, or that they "might as well." Many, and indeed most, divorcees who quickly remarry rush from one unsatisfactory situation to another, largely because they carry their troubles with them and within themselves.

The Child in Trouble. Like their parents, children at one time or another find themselves in what to them is a difficult situation. Things are seldom as bad as they seem, but the child may need assistance, and so may the family. Both may become angry, hysterical or desperate, particularly if they think the family is likely to be "disgraced." If you are asked for advice, try to keep this from happening or from continuing, if it has already begun when you are asked to help. Ascertain facts, then consider with the family how the whole situation, not one acute phase alone, should be handled. Focus on the factual situation and the welfare of the child—not on how the family feel. It is the child in trouble who matters!

If the child is in conflict with the law, and has already been taken to a Juvenile Court, someone will need to interpret to the family and to the child the functions of the court, which represents the child, his needs and responsibilities, as well as the rights of the community—property or personal rights that the child must respect. If home training and parental guidance have not been effective, and the court orders punishment that will impress upon the child (and the family) the seriousness of the offense, the child and the family should be urged to accept this as necessary and justified. Although we are doubtless agreed that, to be just to children, justice must be tempered with mercy, children themselves do not respect the person who is "soft." Unfortunate and sometimes antisocial attitudes are developed in the child who feels that he "got away with it." It may be salutary for him that his first real misconduct became known and was dealt with by an understanding judge.

If the child's trouble can be handled by home or school, it is well to discuss the whole situation fully with him and get his ideas as to what reparation can be made, what punishment he should or should not have. Try to understand and get him to understand why he did a particular thing. Often the child does not know, but through talking with him a sympathetic adult may find out and then handle the situation accordingly. In dealing with children, be sure you are right, then go ahead, but do not act hastily. A little waiting gives everyone concerned time to cool off —time to think rather than feel! A brilliant youngster brought this out as he said thoughtfully that the juvenile detention home where he had spent three days was "the best place in the world; they are my friends; that's where I came to myself!"

Once again, remember that there are people specially trained to deal with such difficulties—psychiatrists and social workers with experience in child guidance. Usually the best thing to do is to get the child and both parents to consult such a person, and then to help them follow the advice given.

Rebellion Against Authority. Do not argue with anyone who is in rebellion, whether child or adult. Wait until fear and anger subside, then point out a reasonable course of action. If possible, present alternative opportunities so that he may feel he still has the power of choice. Help him to find and use his sense of humor; when he laughs at himself the rebellion is over.

Catastrophes. The psychological emergencies we have discussed have been those which affected an individual or his family. Widespread catastrophes, which usually come in the form of war, pestilence, flood or financial disaster, affect a whole community, even the whole world. Each person, however, reacts to a catastrophe as an individual, and with his entire background of habit response and personality. Individuals are likely to meet catastrophes by either over-activity or under-activity; they run around in a circle accomplishing nothing or else sit down and make no effort to better things. Both reactions are equally unfortunate. When catastrophes occur those who can keep calm and think intelligently should show others that we are all in the same boat, that only by working together can any survive. By intelligent, directed and concerted effort people can retrieve almost any situation. It is frequently best not to attempt to re-establish the same conditions that existed prior to the catastrophe, but to utilize the misfortune as a steppingstone to improvement. Man must find new and still more effective methods of dealing with his problems, which are neglected during periods of success and dealt with only when defeat threatens. It is during a catastrophe that human beings realize the uselessness and tyranny of material possessions, as well as discover the true value and beauty of an indomitable spirit. We must help others to meet these situations by going to work ourselves and by encouraging them to see beyond the immediate present, to believe in the future. When we can do this, we can even laugh and sing as we engage busily in constructive planning and working out of what seemed hopeless—a tangible evidence of our faith.

Your best opportunity for showing true leadership comes when a number of people are suffering together. A wise leader can here employ the sustaining influence of group psychology. Discourage discussion of the extent of the catastrophe by helping to initiate remedies which can be quickly accomplished, indicating permanent improvements which will later result as a consequence of the necessary rearrangements. Try to keep everyone busy helping; make people feel needed and important, and stimulate them to new evidence of unselfishness. Since each member of the family is important to the morale of others, make your strongest appeals for help to the weakest members of the group. The strong will stand anyway.

Catastrophes always bring out unexpected courage, resourcefulness and ability. Most people have unsuspected talents lying hidden beneath a crust of repressions, restrictive rearing, education and social taboos; a catastrophe breaks through this crust and the real person has a chance to function. When this happens, give the individual every opportunity to make his contribution; give him full credit for his work, and help him not to go back into his shell when the emergency is over. If a crisis reveals an unsuspected ability in an individual, help him to use that ability to the utmost. Unsuspected emotional needs may also be uncovered in a crisis. For example, the stern, self-sufficient, managerial father will in crisis reveal the need for affection, love and the nearness of his family. Encourage the family to respond and meet this need with love and affection—not only for the duration of the crisis but after the emergency is over.

When people are called upon to work as a group, a certain amount of propaganda is frequently necessary, a presentation of the situation in such a manner as to make them *want* to work together. But it must be a truthful, sincere awakening of group interest, free of sophistry, fear, hatred and jealousy. Group activities at the time of disaster should be the result of generosity, kindness and unselfishness. On such occasions people often have impulsive ideas that do not show very good judgment. A good leader is careful not to squelch these suggestions. Sometimes people are close to despair, and if you belittle their ideas they will give up completely. You can say, "Fine! But let's defer doing that for a moment, while we all do this." Help them join in the common task and welcome their assistance. It is interesting to see how well children behave under real hardships shared with the group. They demonstrate a maturity which they do not ordinarily display—perhaps because under usual conditions parents have a tendency to keep them immature. Scouts, high school students and young people's church organizations should be given more opportunity and responsibility in time of disaster. If the family is in serious trouble, the older children should be allowed to take part in ameliorating the situation. Their fresh young minds, untrammeled by failure, frequently have a new and more hopeful point of view, as well as a desire to use their reserves of strength and energy. The young helpers should be used and praised freely for their accomplishment. Many parents over-protect older children at a time when they should be learning the duties and techniques of citizenship. Instead they should be accepted as full members of the group affected by disaster; treated as adults, they will respond on that basis. Children suffer less from what they know than from the unknown which they fear. We should be careful, however, not to ask of them more than they can handle physically and emotionally, and should not let the strain last too long.

Social Upheaval. Society is in a constant state of change; it is never static. These changes are disconcerting, and it takes time to find how to adjust to them. Most people lag a step behind group pressure; those who resent progressive and inevitable changes fall several steps behind group pressure. The inertia of the individual impedes social progress. Necessity then forces sudden and dramatic developments, which may confuse those who were not prepared for change. Under such circumstances a wise friend can sometimes help by urging those affected to adjust quickly and completely to changed conditions; if necessary to change a way of life, to do it immediately and get it over with. He may say to them, in effect, "Encourage a youthful spirit in yourself; youth does not dread change, but welcomes it. Enjoy some of the rewards inherent in every social readjustment by getting on the bandwagon. Be a part of the new order and, by being part of it, help to guide it wisely. Stop kicking against the pricks. Play your hand as it is dealt. Take difficulties in your stride. Take pride in your own flexibility. Proceed into the future with courage, optimism and faith. These, coupled with intelligence, are all you need."

X

Get a Doctor!

EVERY family, at one time or another, comes up against psychological emergencies that must be handled with every ounce of available wisdom. This chapter is for that family. A careful study of its suggestions should help any family member to know what to do when such situations arise.

There are two kinds of psychological emergencies—minor and serious, superficial and deep-seated. The former may be acute, explosive and temporarily disturbing, but they are obviously minor and not deeply significant. An adolescent girl loses her first sweetheart, a young man is unexpectedly fired from his job, a loving married couple are furious with one another. How can you tell the differences between a superficial and a deep-seated difficulty? The following questions may serve as criteria and help you in deciding what to do for any member of your family needing help:

1. Is he a fundamentally sound and dependable person, or one who frequently explodes emotionally?
2. Does he have good judgment?

183

3. Is this a rare episode or merely a recurrence of many similar reactions?
4. Does he quickly recover, or does the upset state persist? How quick and permanent is the comeback?
5. How much sense of humor, and perspective as to values, has he shown in the past?
6. To what extent has it been evident that he can quickly compensate, without deleterious effects, when faced with unexpected losses or frustrating circumstances?

Frequently you will quickly sense that this family member is sound, able and dependable, with a good possibility of comeback. Or you may know that he is a chronically poor adapter, one who emphasizes trouble. And then you ask yourself: Is this a minor situation or a major one?

You yourself can undoubtedly soothe a minor emotional hurt, support a minor spiritual wilting, and help a strong person to a quick recovery, but if he does not respond quickly and permanently—*get a doctor.*

If he is unstable, one with a life history of trouble, or if the psychological difficulty might possibly become serious—*get a doctor.*

If in doubt, take care of the immediate need—and *get a doctor!*

Fortunately, there are psychiatrists throughout the country nearly always available in an emergency. Psychiatry is now the third largest medical specialty. But be sure to get a good psychiatrist, and if you are in doubt about him, get in touch with your family doctor and ask his help. Indeed, it is a good plan always to go through the family doctor in securing psychiatric assistance. He knows the patient, the family and, usually, the psychiatrist better than you do.

A *psychiatrist* is a graduate physician who has interned in the practice of medicine and has had five years' training in psychological medicine. If possible, get a doctor who is a diplomate of the American Board of Psychiatry.

Remember—a *psychologist* is not a physician. He lacks all medical knowledge, may not prescribe medicine or perform physical examinations, and does not have hospital privileges. Any psychologist who attempts to practice psychiatry is guilty of quackery, so get a doctor of medicine with psychiatric training—not a psychologist.

Why not call the minister? By all means do so if help is needed in the spiritual field and if the minister will cooperate with a doctor (and practically all will). When patient and family are unwilling to see a psychiatrist, the minister is a wonderful person to help. They are all understanding and helpful, be they Catholic priests, Protestant ministers or Jewish rabbis. Try also to get a psychiatrist who is willing to work with them.

Psychiatrists may pass their qualifying boards and yet not be good enough for this particular situation, so you might consider these additional criteria:

1. Do his medical colleagues unhesitatingly recommend him?

2. Is he a person of broad experience?

3. Is he conscientious?

4. Is he persistent, and does he stick by a job until it is accomplished?

5. Does he have initiative, and is he resourceful in finding solutions?

6. Does he listen and give his patient as well as his patient's family plenty of time?

7. Is he available? A good doctor will find time to meet an emergency no matter how busy he is.

There are four kinds of psychiatrists:

1. The Old-Fashioned Type. They have worked in some mental clinic or state hospital, or they may be excellent neurologists doing psychiatry as a side line (many neurologists are excellent psychiatrists). They, like doctors in other specialties, do not generally give the emotionally sick person great and lasting help.

2. The Physiological Psychiatrist. He gives electric shock or insulin or resorts to the organic procedures in preference to other therapies. These physiological treatments are frequently needed and often work miracles, but beware of a doctor whose reputation is based solely on them.

3. The Psychoanalytical Psychiatrist. He has been trained in one of the various schools of psychoanalysis. Formerly he insisted that analysis was the preferred treatment. Recently the able psychoanalyst has come to consider that analysis is only one method of treatment—that in many cases other forms of psychiatric treatment are

preferable. So if you get an analyst in time of emergency, be sure he considers that analysis should be limited to relatively few patients—and that he is a doctor who gets results.

4. The Eclectic Psychiatrist. He has an all-around training and is interested in both medicine and neurology. He can diagnose organic emotional disturbances, he uses physiological treatment wisely and rarely, and he is dynamically (psychoanalytically) oriented. He has a reputation of getting people well quickly with a high percentage of lasting good results.

In general, you can trust a doctor who has been certified by the American Board of Psychiatry and Neurology.

Insist that the patient see a psychiatrist. If necessary, take him, and you yourself talk with the doctor. See that the patient continues to see the psychiatrist.

And if you come to believe that the psychiatrist is not the one this patient should have, get the family doctor to arrange for consultation and perhaps transfer.

But remember, emotionally disturbed patients may need time to understand what their doctor is doing for them. And ordinarily it is a poor plan to shop around from one doctor to another. So try to help them find a good doctor to begin with. If you recommend that they see a psychiatrist and it turns out to be unnecessary, no harm is done. The average layman cannot distinguish measles from scarlet fever, or mental measles from dangerous hysteria—better leave these matters in trained and experienced hands.

XI

Your Mental Hygiene Creed

WE have now covered most of the usual emotional problems—and specific psychological emergencies—you are likely to encounter. And we have discussed techniques geared to solve your personal emotional difficulties and those of relatives or friends needing your help. This, then, is a logical time to recapitulate what we have learned into what might be termed your Mental Hygiene Creed.

But first it is essential for you to realize that you will not always dwell upon the mountain-top; you will sometimes descend into the valley, become discouraged and question your ability to help yourself or to help others. When this time comes, remember that this is a mood, and that by intelligent thinking and acting you can in a few minutes change your mood, regain your optimism and self-confidence.

Now let's review the principles of mental hygiene which you have learned and put into practice, and which you know are effective. Taken together, they form an invaluable Mental Hygiene Creed—one you can refer to time and time again and live by for the rest of your life:

1. I believe in God, and with His help I will make my life significant.
2. I will adapt to life immediately, completely and gracefully.
3. I will work, rest, exercise, play—every day.
4. I will work at a worthwhile job.
5. I will avoid undue fatigue.
6. I will laugh more every day.
7. I will form good habits of living, thinking, acting, speaking and feeling.
8. I believe: that self-pity, suspicion, envy, jealousy and revenge, are useless sentiments. That loyalty, courage and kindness are dependable sentiments; in them I will put my trust.
9. I will discount harmful emotional urges, avoid emotional orgies, and keep away from emotionally undisciplined people.
10. I will face facts, discount my likes and dislikes, and cultivate an objective point of view.
11. I will know myself, accept my liabilities, and cultivate my assets.
12. I will make clear-cut decisions and abide by them. I will ask for counsel, and consider it without argument, but let *no one* make up my mind for me.
13. I do not expect to get precisely what I want in this world. I will not kick against the pricks of life. I expect trouble and have accepted inevitable difficulty, that I may be free to accept opportunity unhandicapped by a sense of difficulties.

14. I know that fear, anxiety and worry cannot hurt me. They threaten to destroy, but they possess no weapons other than the ones I give them. Even though afraid, anxious and worried, I shall continue with my usual activities, knowing that fear is the normal stimulus to courage.

15. I *choose* to see the good aspects and meanings of life. I do not deny that ugliness and evil exist; I do not overlook them, but having seen them *I choose to look for the good.*

16. I know and will help others to remember that humanity is a vast reservoir of love, courage, helpfulness, strength and ability. I shall draw on it without limit to help others and myself.

4